OFFICIAL SQA PAST PAPERS
WITH SQA ANSWERS

Standard Grade
General and Credit
ENGLISH

G Reading 1995 to 1998 and 2000 to 2001
C Reading 1996 to 2001
F/G/C Writing 1999 to 2001
with three years' answers or answer tips

© Copyright Scottish Qualifications Authority

Ist Exam paper published in 1995

Published by
Leckie & Leckie Ltd, 8 Whitehill Terrace, St. Andrews, Scotland KY16 8RN
tel: 01334 475656 fax: 01334 477392
hq@leckieandleckie.co.uk www.leckieandleckie.co.uk

Leckie & Leckie Project Management Team: Tom Davie; David Nicoll; Bruce Ryan
Cover Design Assistance: Mike Middleton

ISBN 1-898890-59-5

A CIP Catalogue record for this book is available from the British Library.

Printed in Scotland by Inglis Allen on environmentally friendly paper. The paper is made from a mixture of sawmill waste, forest thinnings and wood from sustainable forests.

® Leckie & Leckie is a registered trademark.

INVESTOR IN PEOPLE Leckie & Leckie Ltd achieved the Investors in People Standard in 1999.

Leckie & Leckie

Introduction

The best way to prepare for exams is to practise, again and again, all that you have learned over the past year. Work through these questions and check your solutions against these *official SQA answers*. But give yourself a real chance and be honest! Make sure you work through each question thoroughly so that you understand how you got the right answer – *you will have to do this in the exam*!

Leckie & Leckie's Standard Grade English Course Notes. Self-expression has many advantages in school, work and our personal lives. These notes help you study and develop reading, writing and talking skills for all occasions.

Contents

Leckie & Leckie has made every effort to trace all copyright holders. If any have been inadvertently overlooked, Leckie & Leckie will be pleased to make the necessary arrangements. Leckie & Leckie would like to thank the following for their permission to reproduce their material:

John Tierney for an article from the *New York Times* (p 36),
SMG publishing for an article from *The Herald* and Lesley Donald for the accompanying photograph (p 48),
Catherine Czerkawska for an article from *The Scotsman* and *The Scotsman* for the accompanying photo (p 60),
Extract from *Excursions In The Real World* by William Trevor published by Hutchinson. Used by permission of the Random House Group Limited (p 120),
Sally and Richard Greenhill for two photographs (p 144),
Cindy Palmano for a photograph (p 146),
Things can only get better Words and music by Jamie Petrie and Peter Cunnah © 1992 EMI Music Publishing Ltd, London WC2H 0QY (p 166),
BMG Music Publishing for a line from *Search for the Hero* by M People (p 166),
Let me entertain you Words and music by Robert Williams and Guy Chambers © 1997 EMI Virgin Music Ltd, London WC2H 0QY (p 166),
Carcanet Press Ltd for two lines from *Miracle on St David's St* from *Selected Poems* by Gillian Clarke (p 166),
Polygon Press for 4 lines from *The Storyteller* by Liz Lochead (p 166),
JM Dent for two lines from *Poem in October* by Dylan Thomas (p 166),
Michael Busselle for a photograph from *Better Picture Guide to Black and White Photography* (p 172),
Magnum for a photograph by Henri Cartier-Bresson (p 174).

0860/34

SCOTTISH
CERTIFICATE OF
EDUCATION
1995

WEDNESDAY, 3 MAY
1.00 PM – 1.50 PM

ENGLISH
STANDARD GRADE
General Level
Reading
Text

Read carefully the passage overleaf. It will help if you read it twice. When you have done so, answer the questions. Use the spaces provided in the Question/Answer booklet.

SCOTTISH
EXAMINATION
BOARD

MCB 0860/34 6/72610

©

Timothy, Jane, and their mother, Rose, have found an old cottage with a sign: "FOR RENT OR SALE. APPLY TO BEACH HOUSE, WALLNEY." The children have persuaded Rose—against her better judgement—to enquire about renting it, even though it has stood empty for years.

1   Quarter of a mile up the path, they came to the village of Wallney. Not much of a village: four big farmhouses, a couple of rows of flint-and-brick cottages, pub, sub-post office and an old-fashioned red phone-box. But enough to half-restore Rose's sanity. The owner of the cottage wouldn't want to let it just for a week, or even a fortnight. This was no holiday cottage. The thought brought relief.

2   But there stood Beach House, one of the four farmhouses. Well kept, but not a working farm. Weeds grew in front of the barn doors. Rose walked up the tidy front garden, and knocked on the door of the little glass porch. Too late, she realised the front door was never used. The porch was full of potted plants, several big ones right in front of the door itself.

3   An inner door opened, and a grey-haired woman in spectacles appeared. Respectable-dowdy, with sharp blue eyes and a very stubborn mouth. She gestured angrily, indicating some other entrance that should be used. It put poor Rose one-down from the start. She blundered for a long time round the barns and farmyard, trying to find a way through, until finally the woman opened a door in a six-foot wall, and looked at her as if she was an idiot.

4   "We've come," faltered Rose, "about renting the cottage. Only for a week or a fortnight . . ." She was almost ready to take to her heels and run. Only the small eager figures on each side of her kept her steady.

5   "Oh, come in," said the woman impatiently, and led the way with vigorous but erratic steps, as if she had arthritis but was trying to trample it underfoot by sheer will-power.

6   The kitchen they were led into was uncannily like the one they had just seen in the old cottage, except it was shining and alive. There was a glowing coal fire, which cheered Rose up, even in the middle of July. A grandfather clock ticked soothingly. There was a bundle of knitting in a chair, and a tray laid for tea, with a glass sugar-basin. Various chairs were occupied by various teddy-bears, one wearing full-size spectacles.

7   And straightaway, Rose was under a spell. This indeed was her granny's kitchen come again. She felt very small, but very safe.

8   "Sit down, sit down," said the woman irritably.

9   They sat, careful not to inconvenience the teddy-bears.

10   "We're interested in the cottage, Mrs . . ."

11   "Miss," said the woman decisively, as if that disposed of marriage for good and all. "Miss Yaxley. Were you thinking of renting or buying? Renting is thirty pounds a week; buying is fifteen thousand including the furniture thrown in."

12   Rose gasped at such bluntness.

13   "What's it called?"

14   "Beach Cottage. Belonged to my brother. Just inherited it under his will. *I've* got no use for it. Takes me all my time to keep this place going, at my time of life. Much too much for me. Much too much."

15   "We thought we'd like to try it for a week . . ." said Rose. "To see if the children like it. Then perhaps . . ."

16   She was sure this woman would sweep away her nonsense with a flood of biting common sense. But Miss Yaxley seemed to be very much in two minds. She turned aside, and rubbed at a tiny spot on the chrome teapot, as if it was annoying her intensely.

17   "It's no place for children," she said in a low voice. "My brother was an old man . . ."

18   "I think it's great," said Timothy, turning on his most charming smile like a searchlight. He had a swift eye for adult indecision. But Rose thought for once Timothy had overreached himself. Miss Yaxley gave him a grim look, as if to say children should be seen but not heard. She seemed to come to a decision and Rose was sure the answer would be no.

19   So she was all the more amazed when Miss Yaxley said, "Very well. I don't suppose a week can do any harm." She was still vigorously rubbing away at the spot on the teapot, which showed no sign of moving. Then she said, rather grudgingly but also rather guiltily, "I'll only charge twenty pounds for the first week. You'll have to clean the place up. Men live in *such* a muddle. They're *hopeless*. But I'd like the rent in advance. Weekly in advance."

20   There was more thissing and thatting, but in the end Miss Yaxley drove them back herself in her battered Morris Minor with the dry bird-droppings turning into rust-stains on the bonnet. Rose thought that, having made her mind up, Miss Yaxley was not only keen to get them into the cottage, but also curiously keen to get rid of them.

21   They were done and settled in by nine. The children had truly amazed her. Rose was astonished that children could work so hard. Still, the whole thing *had* been their idea.

22   Timothy, who was practical like his Dad, had discovered a drum of paraffin in a lean-to, filled the oil-lamps and got them going. He used more paraffin, in a careful calculating way that brought her out in a cold sweat, to get the fire in the kitchen range going. He had also got the water-pump over the sink to work. At first it had only made disgusting wheezing sounds, but Tim had poured water down it from a butt in the garden, calling it "priming the pump" very professionally. At first it had pumped evil rusty red stuff, but now it ran clear, though Rose had visions of outbreaks of cholera and typhoid, and hurried dashes to the hospital in Norwich, and how would you ever get an ambulance up that path, but if you boiled all the water . . . Now he was winding up all the clocks and really getting them ticking.

23   And Jane had sweated up the path many times with the luggage and then gone with a huge list of groceries to the sub-post office, and staggered back again, still without complaint, and even thought to buy all available hot-water bottles. And boiled huge black kettles, and shoved all the hotties into the beds, which did seem quite clean, thank God, only awfully dusty and sneeze-making. Now she used the black kettle again to make tea, and settled down to drink hers.

24   "We're a nine-days' wonder in the village," she announced. "Everybody staring at me and yak, yak, yak behind their hands. The woman in the shop asked me how long we were staying, and when I said only a week to start with she said, 'Just as well, my girl, just as well.' What on earth do you think she meant by that?"

Adapted from *Yaxley's Cat* by Robert Westall

[END OF PASSAGE]

[BLANK PAGE]

Total Mark

0860/35

SCOTTISH
CERTIFICATE OF
EDUCATION
1995

WEDNESDAY, 3 MAY
1.00 PM – 1.50 PM

**ENGLISH
STANDARD GRADE**
General Level
Reading
Questions

MCB 0860/35 6/72610

SCOTTISH
EXAMINATION
BOARD

Marks

QUESTIONS

Write your answers in the spaces provided.

Look at Paragraph 1.

1. **Write down two** pieces of information which show that Wallney was "not much of a village".

    (i) _____

    (ii) _____

    2 1 0

2. How can you tell from this paragraph that Rose did **not** want to rent the cottage?

    _____

    _____

    2 1 0

Look at Paragraph 2.

3. **Write down two** pieces of information which show that Beach House was "well kept, but not a working farm".

    2 1 0

    (i) Well kept _____

    (ii) Not working _____

4. Explain fully how Rose could tell that "the front door was never used".

    _____

    _____

    2 1 0

Look at Paragraphs 3 to 5.

5. Miss Yaxley seemed unfriendly. **Write down two** expressions which show this.

    2 1 0

    (i) _____

    (ii) _____

6. Describe, **in your own words, two** ways in which Rose was affected by Miss Yaxley's behaviour.

    _____

    _____

    _____

    2 1 0

PAGE
TOTAL

Marks

Look at Paragraphs 6 to 12.

7. The kitchen was "alive". How does the writer develop this idea in the rest of Paragraph 6?

_____

_____

_____ | 2 | 1 | 0 |

8. Explain fully why Rose felt "very small, but very safe". (Paragraph 7)

_____

_____ | 2 | 1 | 0 |

Look at Paragraph 15.

9. (*a*) From the way Rose spoke, what can you tell about her feelings?

_____

_____ | 2 | ■ | 0 |

(*b*) How does the writer show this?

_____

_____ | 2 | 1 | 0 |

Look at Paragraphs 16 to 18.

10. (*a*) Explain, **in your own words,** how Rose expected Miss Yaxley to react to her enquiry.

_____

_____ | 2 | 1 | 0 |

(*b*) How in fact did Miss Yaxley react? Explain as fully as you can.

_____

_____ | 2 | 1 | 0 |

PAGE
TOTAL

Marks

11. Describe **two** ways in which Timothy tried to persuade Miss Yaxley to let them rent the cottage.

(i) _____

(ii) _____

| 2 | 1 | 0 |

12. What made Rose think that Timothy had "overreached himself"? Explain **in your own words**.

_____

_____

_____

| 2 | 1 | 0 |

Look at Paragraph 19.

13. "I'll only charge twenty pounds for the first week." Why did Miss Yaxley say this

(*a*) "rather grudgingly"? _____

_____

| 2 | ■ | 0 |

(*b*) "rather guiltily"? _____

_____

| 2 | ■ | 0 |

Look at Paragraph 22.

14. Give **three** pieces of evidence which show that Timothy was "practical like his Dad".

(i) _____

(ii) _____

(iii) _____

| 2 | 1 | 0 |

15. Write down one expression which shows that Timothy knew what he was doing.

_____

| 2 | ■ | 0 |

PAGE
TOTAL

Marks

16. Look at the sentence beginning "At first it had pumped evil rusty red stuff . . .".
Show how the writer creates an impression of uneasy thoughts rushing through Rose's mind

    (*a*) by word choice. _____

_____ 2 | 1 | 0

    (*b*) by sentence structure. _____

_____ 2 | 1 | 0

Look at Paragraph 23.

17. Write down one word or expression which shows that Jane worked hard.

_____ 2 | ■ | 0

18. Why do you think the writer has used the word "and" so often in the first two sentences of this paragraph?

_____

_____ 2 | 1 | 0

Think about the whole passage.

19. Think carefully of all you learn about Miss Yaxley.

Tick (√) **one** word from the list below which **you** think describes her best, and give a reason for your choice.

| excitable | | | friendly | | | unusual | |

| greedy | | | patient | |

_____

_____

_____ 2 | 1 | 0

PAGE
TOTAL

20. The woman in the shop told Jane it was "just as well" they were staying at the cottage for only a week to start with. (Paragraph 24)

From your reading of the whole passage, explain as fully as you can what **you** think she meant by that.

_____

_____

_____

_____ **2 1 0**

[END OF QUESTION PAPER]

PAGE
TOTAL

FOR OFFICIAL USE

p2 ☐

p3 ☐

p4 ☐

p5 ☐

p6 ☐

TOTAL
MARK ☐

0860/103

SCOTTISH
CERTIFICATE OF
EDUCATION
1996

TUESDAY, 7 MAY
1.00 PM – 1.50 PM

ENGLISH
STANDARD GRADE
General Level
Reading
Text

Read carefully the passage overleaf. It will help if you read it twice. When you have done so, answer the questions. Use the spaces provided in the Question/Answer booklet.

SCOTTISH
EXAMINATION
BOARD

The following article has been adapted from "The Scotsman" newspaper, June 1994.

Washed

1   TWO seagulls hang in the blue sky overhead. For a moment or two they are motionless beneath the white wisps of cloud. One turns its head and screams something to its mate, some seagull joke about the sanity of those humans in the water perhaps.

2   It is 3pm on Saturday and at this precise moment there are three people in the open-air swimming pool at North Berwick, tiny figures bobbing about in the vast blue expanse of water. There are many more shivering beneath towels around the perimeter. The pool was one of the town's most important tourist attractions. They had galas here, swimming and diving displays that pulled in big crowds.

3   It still has its regulars. Two old women turn up with raincoats over their swimming costumes, so they can get into the pool as quickly as possible. Two old men do synchronised swimming. Others bring the staff sweets or baking. But numbers have been falling for years. Costs are high and the season is short. East Lothian District Council is subsidising the swimmers to the tune of almost £10 a time.

4   Now the council has decided to build a modern indoor pool and close one of Scotland's last remaining open-air pools. It has been there since 1900, an essential part of the North Berwick landscape for generations of holiday-makers.

There was a time when almost every swimming-pool, but now long-term future is threatened.

5   There was a time when almost every seaside resort had an outdoor pool, overflowing with noisy, splashing bodies in the summer months. They were part of Scotland. They are part of our social history. But the bodies have disappeared into leisure pools and onto charter flights to Majorca, and the open-air pools have disappeared in their wake.

6   Anstruther, Arbroath, Buckhaven, Macduff, Prestwick, Saltcoats; they all had their own pools. There must have been dozens of them once. There were separate men's and women's pools at St Andrews, but mixed bathing was widely accepted by the time most pools were built in the Thirties when interest in healthy outdoor activities took off.

Cool customers: there is a breeze sweeping across the pool and the teenagers are shivering violently. But then that is because they are speaking to a journalist and not in the warmed water.

away

Scottish seaside resort had an outdoor
there are only a few and their
BRIAN PENDREIGH reports

7   Portobello Pool opened in 1936 and was considered one of the wonders of the age. It had a diving platform 33 ft above the water, four chutes, four springboards and band music was relayed from Princes Street Gardens. The wave machine was so powerful it soaked the poolside dignitaries on the opening day.

8   The pool became a national attraction and there were 18,000 admissions on a single day, just 4,000 fewer than the number of admissions for the whole of the pool's final summer in 1978. Particularly in the early days, many went merely to spectate or sunbathe, though, unlike some pools, Portobello was heated from the outset, using steam from the adjoining power station. Sean Connery worked as a lifeguard for a while. Now both pool and power station have gone.

9   North Berwick pool will probably open in 1995 for the last time. Other outdoor pools survive at Stonehaven and Gourock, but neither's long-term future is secure.

10   Stonehaven had 86,000 admissions in 1934, its first year, though three-quarters were spectators. Initially the water was unheated, untreated seawater, changed every few days "as it became dirty". The following year it was filtered, disinfected and heated, and the number of people actually going into the pool almost doubled.

11   In 1990, there were 25,000 admissions. In 1993 there were 14,000. The decline would be worse if it were not for the successful reintroduction of special midnight swimming sessions, which had been abandoned in the Seventies because of drunkenness.

12   At North Berwick attendances have fallen steadily over the past five summers, from 21,177 swimmers in 1989 to 8,154 in 1993. "It will be a great sin if this pool closes. This is character-building stuff in here," says Pat Macaulay, who has swum regularly in the pool since childhood and is here with her new season-ticket and her children Richard and Joanna. Pat Macaulay spent the summers of her youth in and by the pool. It was *the* meeting place, *the* social centre for the young people of the town.

13   There is a drop or two of rain in the air and a breeze sweeping across the exposed location beside the harbour. Is it not rather cold? "The water is fine," says Macaulay. "A lot of it is mind over matter . . . I think the kids are getting a bit soft these days."

14   But there are few adults in evidence at this session. The vast majority are children and teenagers, who form lines by the chute and springboard at the deep end.

15   They complain that the new leisure pools do not have these features, the new pools are smaller and the Royal Commonwealth Pool too far away. They are shivering violently. "That's because we're out here speaking to you," says one. "When you're in it's brilliant." Journalistic integrity demands his claim be put to the test.

16   It is not the cold that hits you, but the mouthful of salt water, as you disappear beneath the surface for the first time. The pool is heated, though not as warm as some indoor pools. But some indoor pools are too warm for strenuous swimming. North Berwick is fine as long as you keep moving. There is something quite pleasant in swimming along on your back listening to the chat of the gulls. It is cold when you get out. The knack is to get dried immediately afterwards and not hang around talking to journalists.

17   Shona MacDonald, the pondmaster, and her assistant Michelle Smith have an enormous affection for North Berwick. "The people love it here," Smith says. "We would buy it ourselves if we had the money."

18   However, East Lothian's director of leisure and tourism, says: "Outdoor pools are very expensive to run and declining in terms of attractiveness."

19   The council is building an indoor pool at Musselburgh and is not reopening the outdoor pool at nearby Port Seton. Work has begun on a £2 million pool beside North Berwick's sports centre with opening scheduled for 1996. It will be open all the year round and is expected to have at least 75,000 admissions annually.

20   The director accepts there is some regret in the town at the decision to close the open-air pool, but adds that there have been no formal protests. "People are just being rather nostalgic. The pool has had its day. It's part of a former era."

21   Within the next few years the area occupied by the open-air pool may be returned to its natural state of rocks and sea. The gulls will have a different landscape to discuss. Only rocks and sea remain forever, but the old landscape will undoubtedly linger in the memory of all those whose guts filled with seawater on a chilly Scottish summer's day.

[END OF PASSAGE]

[BLANK PAGE]

G

Total Mark

0860/104

SCOTTISH
CERTIFICATE OF
EDUCATION
1996

TUESDAY, 7 MAY
1.00 PM – 1.50 PM

ENGLISH
STANDARD GRADE
General Level
Reading
Questions

SCOTTISH
EXAMINATION
BOARD

MCB 0860/104 6/69210

©

Marks

QUESTIONS

Write your answers in the spaces provided.

Look at Paragraphs 1 to 4.

1. According to the writer, what might the seagulls think of the people in the water?

    _____   2 ▪ 0

2. In Paragraph 2, the writer tells us that there are only three people in the water. Why do you think he also mentions the exact time, and the day?

    _____   2 ▪ 0

3. **Write down** an expression which emphasises the size of the open-air pool at North Berwick.

    _____   2 ▪ 0

4. How can you tell that there are no longer galas at the pool?

    _____   2 ▪ 0

5. Give **two** reasons why East Lothian District Council decided to close the open-air pool.   2 1 0

    (i) _____

    (ii) _____

6. The open-air pool has been "an essential part of the North Berwick landscape for generations of holiday-makers".

    Write down an expression from earlier in this section which conveys the same idea.

    _____

    _____   2 ▪ 0

Look at Paragraphs 5 and 6.

7. "There was a time when almost every seaside resort had an outdoor pool . . ."

    Explain how the writer continues this idea in paragraph 6.

    _____

    _____

    _____   2 1 0

PAGE
TOTAL

8. **In your own words**, explain the reasons given for the disappearance of open-air pools.

_____

_____

_____   2 1 0

Look at Paragraphs 7 and 8.

9. **Write down three** pieces of information which show why Portobello Pool was considered "one of the wonders of the age".   2 1 0

   (i) _____

   (ii) _____

   (iii) _____

10. **Write down** an expression which shows that Portobello Pool was popular with people from all over the country.

_____

_____   2 ■ 0

Look at Paragraphs 10 and 11.

11. **In your own words**, give **two** reasons why the number of swimmers at Stonehaven Pool increased in 1935.   2 1 0

   (i) _____

   (ii) _____

12. What was the effect of the "reintroduction of special midnight swimming sessions"?

_____

_____   2 1 0

Look at Paragraphs 12 and 13.

13. How do the attendance **figures** given in paragraph 12 show that the writer is closely interested in North Berwick Pool?

_____   2 ■ 0

PAGE TOTAL

Marks

14. Pat Macaulay says, "This is character-building stuff in here".
Write down something else she says which continues this idea.

_____   2 ■ 0

15. "It was *the* meeting place, *the* social centre . . ." (Paragraph 12)
The writer uses italics to show that the word "*the*" has a particular meaning here.
What do you think that meaning is?

_____   2 ■ 0

Look at Paragraphs 14 to 16.

16. What things do young people dislike about the new leisure pools?

_____

_____   2 1 0

17. "When you're in it's brilliant." (Paragraph 15)

(*a*) How does the writer test this claim?

_____   2 ■ 0

(*b*) Explain why he feels the need to test it.

_____

_____   2 1 0

18. (*a*) **Write down two** things the writer seems to like about North Berwick Pool.   2 1 0

(i) _____

(ii) _____

(*b*) **Write down two** things he seems to dislike about it.   2 1 0

(i) _____

(ii) _____

PAGE
TOTAL

Marks

Look at Paragraph 20.

19. "... there is some regret ... at the decision to close the open-air pool"

    (a) **Write down** another expression from this paragraph which indicates people's feelings about the closure.

    _____

    2 ■ 0

    (b) Explain **in your own words** what this expression tells you about people's feelings.

    _____

    _____

    2 1 0

Think about the passage as a whole.

20. This article was taken from a newspaper.

    Write down any **three** features of it which are typical of a newspaper article.

    2 1 0

    (i) _____

    (ii) _____

    (iii) _____

21. Explain how the title relates to the content of the passage.

    _____

    _____

    _____

    2 1 0

22. (a) What unusual idea does the writer use at the beginning and ending of the passage?

    _____

    _____

    2 1 0

    (b) What effect does this have?

    _____

    _____

    2 ■ 0

[*END OF QUESTION PAPER*]

PAGE TOTAL

FOR OFFICIAL USE

p2 ☐

p3 ☐

p4 ☐

p5 ☐

TOTAL
MARK ☐

G

0860/103

SCOTTISH
CERTIFICATE OF
EDUCATION
1997

WEDNESDAY, 7 MAY
1.00 PM – 1.50 PM

**ENGLISH
STANDARD GRADE**
General Level
Reading
Text

Read carefully the passage overleaf. It will help if you read it twice. When you have done so,
answer the questions. Use the spaces provided in the Question/Answer booklet.

SCOTTISH
QUALIFICATIONS
AUTHORITY

Tunes For Bears To Dance To

1   Henry had been impatient for the cast to be removed so that he could return to his job as the bender for Mr Hairston at the Corner Market. Mr Hairston had a back problem and found it hard to bend over. Henry did the bending for him. Picked up whatever fell on the floor. Reached for merchandise on the lower shelves to fill the customers' orders. He also had other duties. Helped unload the boxes and crates that arrived from the wholesalers. Stocked the shelves. Bagged the potatoes in the cellar, then carried them upstairs to the produce section. Mr Hairston was proud of his produce. Fresh lettuce and carrots and spinach and such extras as parsnips and mushrooms, all of them in neat display at the rear of the store.

2   Henry worked at the store every day after school and on Saturday mornings. Until, that is, he had broken his kneecap, tripping, then falling down the bottom steps of the house just as school ended in June. A hair-line fracture, the doctor had said, nothing serious, but serious enough for a cast that enclosed his calf and knee. Mr Hairston said he would keep his job open until his knee was healed.

3   "How will you bend over?" Henry had asked.

4   "I won't stock the lower shelves until you come back."

5   "Who'll sweep the floors and put up the potatoes?"

6   Mr Hairston had scowled without answering. He scowled most of the time, his expression as sour as the pickles in the wooden barrel near the cash register.

7   Five weeks later when Henry reported to the store without his crutches, ready for work, Mr Hairston merely grunted.

8   "Potatoes to bag up," he called over the shoulder of a customer, and Henry made his way down to the cellar, where a bin of potatoes awaited him. He always tried to hurry the job because the cellar was dark and damp and he often heard rats scurrying across the floor. One day, a grey rat squirted out of a bag of potatoes and Henry had leapt with fright, his heart exploding in his chest. He was afraid of a lot of things — the closet door that never stayed closed in his bedroom, spooky movies about vampires — but most of all, the rats.

9   When he came back upstairs, Mr Hairston was saying goodbye to a customer Henry recognized as Mrs Pierce, who lived on the first floor of his tenement. Smiling and nodding, Mr Hairston led her to the door and closed it softly after her.

10   "Disgusting, the wart on her chin, hairs growing out of it," he said, returning to the register, a sneer replacing the smile. Actually, his smile was merely a rearrangement of his lips, his usual sneer turned inside out. Henry was amazed at how Mr Hairston treated his customers.

11   "The customer's always right," he proclaimed one day, as if he could read Henry's mind. "But only in the store. When buying. Otherwise, they're only people. Stupid, most of them. Don't even know a bargain when they see one. So, why give them a bargain?"

12   He handed Henry a candy bar, which astounded the boy because Mr Hairston had never before given him a treat. "Eat," he said. Then, "It was nice with the customers during the war, though. Rationing. People came running if they heard I had got butter in. Or cigarettes."

13   Henry listened, his cheeks bulging with the candy while Mr Hairston looked off, as if he were talking to himself, his voice almost dreamy. "I'd make them line up. Make them wait, acting like the stuff hadn't arrived yet but was expected any minute. All the time the order was here and they waited in line. I was like a dictator, the way they treated me. I *was* a dictator. Because I had control over them." Then looking down as if discovering Henry's presence after having forgotten him there, he said, "Go to work. I don't pay you to hang around doing nothing."

14   Just before closing time, while Henry was sweeping the floor, Mr Hairston's daughter came into the store. She appeared at the back door, having descended from the tenement above, where Mr Hairston lived with his wife, whom Henry had never seen, and the girl, whose name was Doris. Doris was a whisper of a girl, slender, with long black curls that reached her shoulders, a bow in her hair. It always looked like the same bow but the colours were different, red and yellow and blue, bright and vivid colours in contrast with her pale, white face, the dark eyes deep in their sockets, like the windows of a haunted house.

15   She usually came and went like a ghost, appearing suddenly and then fading away, a door closing softly behind her or the rustle of her clothing faint in the air. Sometimes he didn't see her at all but sensed her presence somewhere in the store. She was a year ahead of him in school and when they met in the corridor she lowered her eyes and looked away. She always carried library books in her arms. In the store he sometimes felt those haunted eyes upon him, turned and almost saw her, then heard the back door closing softly. They had never spoken a word to each other.

16   Whenever Mr Hairston saw her in the store, he would order her to leave. "Upstairs," he'd command, his hand pointing to the ceiling.

17   That afternoon the girl spoke to Henry for the first time, a brief word, "Hello." So brief and whispered that at first he doubted his ears. She didn't smile at him but her expression changed, or rather an expression of some kind filled the usual blankness of her face. He could not read that expression. As she turned away before he could return her greeting — if it *had* been a greeting — he noticed a bruise on her cheek, purple and ugly.

18   "What happened to your cheek?" he asked, whispering for some reason.

19   "Upstairs!"

20   Mr Hairston's voice was like thunder in the quiet store and Henry leapt with surprise as he turned to confront the store owner, whose face was dark with anger.

21   Henry began to sweep furiously and heard the girl's footsteps fading, the door opening and closing.

22   "She fell down," Mr Hairston said while Henry swept the same spot over and over. "Clumsy girl, always hurting herself."

23   A late customer entered the store and Mr Hairston turned away, cursing beneath his breath. He hated last-minute customers.

24   That night Henry thought of Doris, who was clumsy and fell down a lot and hurt herself. He prayed to keep her safe from harm.

Adapted from *Tunes For Bears To Dance To* by Robert Cormier

[END OF PASSAGE]

[BLANK PAGE]

FOR OFFICIAL USE

Presenting Centre No.	Subject No. 0860	Level	Paper No.	Group No.	Marker's No.

Total Mark

0860/104

SCOTTISH
CERTIFICATE OF
EDUCATION
1997

WEDNESDAY, 7 MAY
1.00 PM – 1.50 PM

ENGLISH
STANDARD GRADE
General Level
Reading
Questions

Fill in these boxes and read what is printed below.

Full name of school or college

Town

First name and initials

Surname

Date of birth
Day Month Year

Candidate number

Number of seat

NB Before leaving the examination room you must give this booklet to the invigilator. If you do not, you may lose all the marks for this paper.

SCOTTISH
QUALIFICATIONS
AUTHORITY

©

MCB 0860/104 6/71910

Marks

QUESTIONS

Write your answers in the spaces provided.

Look at Paragraphs 1 and 2.

1. Why had Henry been "impatient"?

   _____

   _____   2 1 0

2. Why did Mr Hairston need a "bender"?

   _____

   _____   2 1 0

3. (a) **Write down three** things Henry did as part of his "other duties".   2 1 0

   (i) _____

   (ii) _____

   (iii) _____

   (b) How does the writer's sentence construction in Paragraph 1 draw attention to the variety of actions Henry has to carry out?

   _____

   _____   2 1 0

Look at Paragraphs 7 and 8.

4. **In your own words** describe how Mr Hairston first greeted Henry on his return to work.

   _____

   _____   2 1 0

5. What **three** things did Henry dislike about the cellar?   2 1 0

   (i) _____

   (ii) _____

   (iii) _____

PAGE
TOTAL

Marks

6. "... a grey rat squirted out of a bag of potatoes ..." (Paragraph 8)

(*a*) What is unusual about the writer's use of the word "squirted" in this sentence?

_____   2 ■ 0

(*b*) Why is it a particularly suitable word to use here?

_____   2 ■ 0

Look at Paragraphs 9 to 11.

7. (*a*) Describe Mr Hairston's **behaviour** and **attitude** towards Mrs Pierce while she
was in his shop.   2 1 0

  (i) Behaviour   _____

  _____

  (ii) Attitude   _____

  _____

(*b*) Explain fully how these changed once she had left.   2 1 0

  (i) Behaviour   _____

  _____

  (ii) Attitude   _____

  _____

8. **Write down** the **one** word the writer uses which most clearly shows that
Mr Hairston's smile was not genuine.

┌─────────────────────────────────┐
│   │
│   │
└─────────────────────────────────┘   2 ■ 0

9. (*a*) What is unusual about the writer's sentence construction in Paragraph 11?

_____   2 ■ 0

(*b*) What does the writer's use of this construction suggest about Mr Hairston's
character?

_____   2 ■ 0

PAGE
TOTAL

Marks

Look at Paragraphs 12 and 13.

10. (a) What was Mr Hairston's **real** reason for thinking "it was nice with the customers during the war"?

    _____   2 1 0

    (b) Give an example of his behaviour which supports your answer to (a).

    _____   2 ■ 0

11. While talking about wartime, Mr Hairston "looked off . . . his voice almost dreamy".
    What else did he do which suggests he had been day-dreaming?

    _____   2 ■ 0

Look at Paragraphs 14 and 15.

12. (a) Doris is described as a "whisper" of a girl.
       What do you think the writer means by this?

    _____   2 ■ 0

    (b) In Paragraph 14, what comparison does the writer use to describe her eyes?

    _____   2 ■ 0

    (c) **Write down three** other words or expressions from Paragraph 15 which the writer uses to convey a similar idea about Doris.   2 1 0

    (i) _____

    (ii) _____

    (iii) _____

13. **Write down** the **two separate words** which best convey the contrast between Doris's face and her bows.

    [   ]   and   [   ]
                                                                                          2 ■ 0

14. Give **two** pieces of evidence which suggest that Doris was shy.   2 1 0

    (i) _____

    (ii) _____

PAGE
TOTAL

Marks

Look at Paragraphs 17 and 18.

15. (a) What unusual thing happened that afternoon?

_____

    2 | 1 | 0

    (b) Explain **in your own words** why Henry "doubted his ears".

_____

_____

    2 | 1 | 0

    (c) **Write down** an expression from later in Paragraph 17 which repeats this idea of doubt.

_____

    2 | ■ | 0

16. When Henry asked Doris about her cheek, he whispered "for some reason".
    What reason do you think he had for whispering?

_____

    2 | ■ | 0

Look at Paragraphs 20 to 24.

17. Mr Hairston's face was "dark with anger".
    What other expression is used in this paragraph to show his anger?

_____

    2 | ■ | 0

18. "Henry began to sweep furiously" (Paragraph 21)
    ". . . Henry swept the same spot over and over" (Paragraph 22)
    What do Henry's actions tell you about how he felt?

_____

_____

    2 | 1 | 0

19. "'She fell down,' Mr Hairston said . . ." (Paragraph 22)
    From your reading of the whole passage, do you believe Mr Hairston? Give a reason for your answer.

_____

_____

_____

_____

    2 | 1 | 0

[END OF QUESTION PAPER]

PAGE
TOTAL

FOR OFFICIAL USE

p2	☐
p3	☐
p4	☐
p5	☐
TOTAL MARK	☐

[BLANK PAGE]

[BLANK PAGE]

0860/103

SCOTTISH
CERTIFICATE OF
EDUCATION
1998

WEDNESDAY, 6 MAY
1.00 PM – 1.50 PM

ENGLISH
STANDARD GRADE
General Level
Reading
Text

Read carefully the passage overleaf. It will help if you read it twice. When you have done so, answer the questions. Use the spaces provided in the Question/Answer booklet.

Why You Don't See Baby Pigeons

1   When I moved to a flat in New York and discovered that my new neighbours included a colony of pigeons, my first reaction was: exterminate the brutes! I cringed at their morning mating calls, and agreed with my wife, Dana, when she cursed them as winged rodents that soil the city. I attacked them with broom and water-pistol. It was hard for me to believe that the traditional symbol of peace, a dove with an olive branch, is actually a white pigeon.

2   Then last December, after scaring away a grey pigeon roosting on the sill of our bathroom window, I found a nest there with an egg in it. "Revenge is ours!" I shouted to Dana, triumphantly holding the egg aloft. "Should I smash it right away or save it for an omelette?"

3   But Dana was looking in horror at the window-sill behind me. The pigeon had swooped back to the empty nest and was beating its wings against the window frame.

4   "You put that back this second!" Dana said, with the same look on her face that I swear the parent pigeon had.

5   "How can a rational human want to save a baby pigeon?" I asked as I returned the egg.

6   And then it came to me. Here was a chance to answer the perennial mystery that puzzled generations of city dwellers: why doesn't anyone ever see a baby pigeon? Let others plumb Loch Ness for its monster or climb the Himalayas in search of the Yeti. I would be the first human to see a baby pigeon in the wild.

7   The bird roosted outside the bathroom for a week, and then one morning the nest was empty—no mother, no baby, no egg. Soon another nest appeared with two eggs, but they, too, vanished.

8   I began keeping a field journal, and named the grey pigeon Medea and her black-and-white speckled partner Don Guano. On March 12 Don Guano strutted about, following Medea in circles around the living-room ledge. Finally he mounted her for a second or two, flapping his wings—for balance, I suppose, unless he was just happy.

9   Two days later an egg appeared, followed shortly by a second. Don Guano and Medea settled into a domestic routine. From late morning until late afternoon he sat on the eggs while she went off. The rest of the time, she roosted while he brought twigs for home-improvement projects.

10   Then, after ten days of roosting, Don Guano and Medea abruptly abandoned the nest. The next day the eggs were gone without a trace.

11   I reported the parenting troubles to Margaret Barker of the Cornell Laboratory of Ornithology. "Eggs normally hatch after 18 days," she said, "but sometimes pigeons are frightened off the nest, and sometimes eggs never hatch because the parents aren't getting the proper diet to make sturdy eggshells."

12   "And why," I asked, "do we never see a baby pigeon?" "They stay in the nest for the first month," Margaret told me, "and grow so rapidly they're nearly full size when they emerge."

13   When Medea returned, I fed her a bowl of cereal mixed with a powdered calcium supplement. I worried about what this was doing to me. Was I becoming one of those people on park benches who feed pigeons?

14   Soon the calcium-enriched Medea laid two more eggs, and this time the roosting proceeded smoothly for the full 18 days. We were ready to make history on Friday, April 21. I armed myself with a new pair of binoculars and a copy of *The Pigeon* by Wendell Mitchell Levi, which I studied with all the care other parents devote to Dr Spock's books.

15   "Wherever civilisation has flourished, there the pigeon has thrived," wrote Levi. Pigeons are found on every continent except Antarctica, inhabiting environments from Alaska to the equatorial islands. They were worshipped in Mesopotamia and sculpted on Egyptian tombs. They carried messages for King Solomon, helped Julius Caesar conquer Gaul and won dozens of medals for combat service during the Second World War.

16   Pigeons, or "rock doves", can fly up to 75 miles per hour and find their way home from more than 1000 miles away. Their primary reference seems to be the position of the sun, which correlates with a pigeon's biological clock. But they can navigate even under overcast skies by sensing the earth's magnetic field. There are "reverse commuter" pigeons, urban pigeons that fly 30 miles a day to fields and grain silos outside the city, then return to roost in town.

17   They are social animals, living in colonies because they gain protection from predators. Poets have praised pigeons' lifelong devotion to their mates. Tennyson linked their iridescent feathers with romance and rebirth in his famous couplet:

In the spring a livelier iris changes on the burnish'd dove;
In the spring a young man's fancy lightly turns to thoughts of love.

18   I quoted those lines to Don Guano and Medea as we waited on that crucial Friday in April. But by evening, neither egg had hatched. I feared the worst. Next day at noon, however, as I watched Don Guano settle in for his shift on the nest, I spotted a bit of golden fuzz moving underneath him.

19   It was a shaggy little creature, lying in a heap along with the eggshell it had just escaped. "Miracle of miracles!" I wrote in my journal. "Yes, New York, there is a baby pigeon." I had never been an animal lover and was not particularly fond of naturalists or the endangered species they were trying to save. So why pigeons?

20   The answer did not occur to me until I visited New York's most glamorous bird, the peregrine falcon, 57 floors above the streets. There was no doubting this bird's power, particularly after seeing the ***pigeon*** feathers in the nest—the remnants of victims captured in mid-air and fed to the falcon chick. But as I looked at the falcons, all I could think was: *You wimps! You wouldn't be here without us! We've spent millions on you; we've banned the DDT that was upsetting your delicate systems; we've built you nest boxes; we've coddled your chicks—all to produce two dozen birds in New York. One pigeon colony achieved that in my courtyard by itself.*

21   A lot of people in the city may identify with the falcon: a ruthless, grandly isolated predator, rewarded with a penthouse view of its dominion. But the falcon doesn't hold the great secret to evolutionary success, at least not for humans.

22   Our species did not prevail over other animals by being brave and cunning solitary hunters. We used our brains to become co-operative and shameless opportunists, able to adapt to any available niche. We may pollute and squabble and crowd together in grimy crannies without views, but at least we're survivors. We may envy their speed and rapacity, but we are not falcons. We are tougher. We, fortunately, are pigeons.

Adapted from a *New York Times* article by John Tierney

[END OF PASSAGE]

[BLANK PAGE]

Total Mark

0860/104

SCOTTISH
CERTIFICATE OF
EDUCATION
1998

WEDNESDAY, 6 MAY
1.00 PM – 1.50 PM

ENGLISH
STANDARD GRADE
General Level
Reading
Questions

Fill in these boxes and read what is printed below.

Full name of school or college

Town

First name and initials

Surname

Date of birth
Day   Month   Year

Candidate number

Number of seat

NB Before leaving the examination room you must give this booklet to the invigilator. If you do not, you may lose all the marks for this paper.

SCOTTISH
QUALIFICATIONS
AUTHORITY

Marks

QUESTIONS

Write your answers in the spaces provided.

Look at Paragraphs 1 to 5.

1. (a) **Write down** an expression from **Paragraph 1** that clearly indicates **the writer's attitude** to pigeons.

   _____   2 ■ 0

   (b) Given his attitude, what **fact** about pigeons did the writer find difficult to understand?

   _____

   _____   2 ■ 0

2. (a) "Should I smash it right away or save it for an omelette?" (Paragraph 2)
   What was Dana's reaction to these suggestions?

   _____

   _____   2 ■ 0

   (b) Why is her reaction surprising?

   _____

   _____   2 1 0

Look at Paragraph 6.

3. Why does the writer begin **Paragraph 6** with such a short sentence?

   _____

   _____

   _____   2 ■ 0

4. What expression used later in the same paragraph means almost the same as "perennial mystery"?

   _____   2 ■ 0

PAGE
TOTAL

5. Explain how the writer tries to make the rest of **Paragraph 6** funny.

_____

_____

_____ | 2 | 1 | 0

Look at Paragraphs 7 to 10.

6. What evidence is there that the writer started to take a closer interest in the pigeons? | 2 | 1 | 0

(i) _____

(ii) _____

(iii) _____

7. "he brought twigs for home-improvement projects" (Paragraph 9)

(*a*) Explain exactly what Don Guano was doing.

_____

_____ | 2 | 1 | 0

(*b*) To what is Don Guano being compared, and what is the effect of this comparison?

_____

_____ | 2 | 1 | 0

Look at Paragraphs 11 to 14.

8. (*a*) Why might pigeon eggs **not** hatch after 18 days? | 2 | 1 | 0

(i) _____

_____

(ii) _____

_____

(*b*) Why don't we normally see a baby pigeon?

_____

_____ | 2 | 1 | 0

Marks

9. What, do you think, was **the writer's attitude** to "those people on park benches who feed pigeons" and how does he reveal it?

_____

_____

_____   **2 1 0**

10. (a) **Write down two** things the writer did to ensure that the eggs hatched successfully.   **2 1 0**

   (i) _____

   (ii) _____

   (b) What kind of books do you think Dr Spock wrote?

   _____

   _____   **2 1 0**

Look at Paragraphs 15 to 18.

11. "Wherever civilization has flourished, there the pigeon has thrived" (Paragraph 15) What fact proves this statement?

_____

_____   **2 1 0**

12. What **two** things help pigeons to navigate?   **2 1 0**

   (i) _____

   (ii) _____

13. Explain why "reverse commuter" is a good way of describing urban pigeons.

_____

_____

_____   **2 1 0**

PAGE
TOTAL

Marks

14. Explain **in your own words** why poets have praised pigeons.

_____

_____   2 | 1 | 0

Look at Paragraphs 19 to 22.

15. (a) Why does the writer call peregrine falcons "wimps"?

_____

_____   2 | 1 | 0

(b) What **two** things about the way **Paragraph 20** is written show the strength of
his feelings?   2 | 1 | 0

   (i) _____

   (ii) _____

16. (a) **In your own words**, explain why a lot of people might "identify with the
falcon".

_____

_____

_____   2 | 1 | 0

(b) Explain, as clearly as you can, why the writer believes that most human beings
are more like pigeons than falcons.

_____

_____   2 | 1 | 0

[Turn over for Questions 17 and 18 on *Page six*

PAGE
TOTAL

Marks

Think about the passage as a whole.

17. Complete the following sentences to show the changes in the writer's attitude towards pigeons.

    (i) To begin with the writer _____ .

    (ii) Later he _____ .

    (iii) Finally he _____ .

| 2 | 1 | 0 |

18. Tick (✓) **one** of the following words and explain why **you** think it is the best one to describe this passage. Give evidence from the passage to support your answer.

informative ☐   surprising ☐   thought-provoking ☐

_____

_____

_____

| 2 | 1 | 0 |

[END OF QUESTION PAPER]

PAGE
TOTAL

FOR OFFICIAL USE

p2	
p3	
p4	
p5	
p6	
TOTAL MARK	

[BLANK PAGE]

0860/403

NATIONAL
QUALIFICATIONS
2000

TUESDAY, 16 MAY
1.00 PM – 1.50 PM

**ENGLISH
STANDARD GRADE**
General Level
Reading
Text

Read carefully the passage overleaf. It will help if you read it twice. When you have done so, answer the questions. Use the spaces provided in the Question/Answer booklet.

SCOTTISH
QUALIFICATIONS
AUTHORITY

The following passage has been adapted from an article in "The Herald".

Just when you thought it was

Stephen McGinty

faces danger to swim with the sharks

1   There is a cartoon in the diver's locker room at Deep Sea World. It shows two sharks eyeing up a couple of divers in masks, fins and aqua-lungs. One shark asks the other, "Will we eat them?" The other replies, "No, that thing on their backs gives me wind."

2   As I bent, buckled and squeezed myself into the drysuit, the threat of a dose of marine indigestion seemed a poor defence against the flat-eyed terrors of the deep.

3   I had been assured at the North Queensferry complex that the sharks would have no wish to eat me. I did not look like their natural prey of fish, which are small, wet and flap about. No-one noticed that at the time I felt small, was drenched in sweat and couldn't stop shaking. I didn't feel like a flounder, but given time . . .

4   In the next chamber was the world's largest underwater safari: four and a half million litres of filtered sea water containing dozens of species and hundreds of fish including bass, cod, plaice, bream, mackerel, lesser spotted dogfish, conger eels, skates and sharks. The nine bigger sharks were sand tigers—the largest about nine feet long.

5   All the sand tigers have names like Stella, Bertha, Fred, Barnie and Dino. The largest is called The Preacher because most people see him and start to pray. Barnie sounded like a bundle of laughs in comparison.

6   "Mind, the big one is a bit frisky," said another diver to Stuart Bell, my scuba instructor.

7   "Frisky?" I nervously asked.

8   "Don't worry," Stuart said as he helped zip up my drysuit. To explain, a wet suit gets you wet; the water enters holes in the suit but doesn't exit, so your body-temperature heats the water, providing an insulating layer. A dry suit seals out the water allowing you to wear tracksuit bottoms and T-shirt underneath for warmth.

9   Once sealed inside our suits, we clambered into a tiny tank, containing only a few crabs, where I hauled on my aqualung and weight belt. Sinking to the bottom I struggled to gain my balance against the backwards pull of the weights and aqualung. Gripping Stuart's arm, I drained the air from the suit and accustomed myself to the sensation of breathing underwater.

10   When I was relaxed, Stuart opened the

Childhood fears are faced as a shark

hatch leading to the main safari tank. Rock walls dropped to the sandy floor 30 feet below.

11   Though the habitat felt natural, it would be impossible to view such a variety of sea-life in Scotland's brackish waters. Brightly coloured fish of greens, blues and greys darted, twisted and turned, and a giant skate flapped over the tunnel as tourists, wide-eyed in wonder, peered up as I looked down into an utterly silent world. The only sound was the rasp of my own breath and the click of swallowing.

12   Stuart descended first and I quickly followed squinting while the pressure built in my ears. Just as on an aeroplane, you can clear them by pinching your nose and blowing. On the bottom I lost balance but was supported by Stuart as I found my feet.

13   Childhood memories of underwater programmes on TV flooded in, mixing with books and magazines on sharks and the film cartoon of *Marine Boy*. Once I had gained some confidence, Stuart returned to the surface to collect underwater photographer Gavin Anderson. It was then I noticed the little four-year-old waving from the tunnel. I started to think: what if I was eaten by a nine-foot shark? Would it scar him for life? Then I put myself in his place. As a small child my only response to a diver being savaged to death by a giant shark just feet in front of me would be . . . COOOOOL!!!

[0860/403]

safe to go to North Queensferry

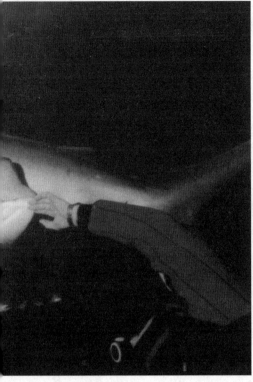

swims by, close enough to touch.

14 Deep Sea World was drawing them in with a blood-curdling exhibition about pirates. Just how much would the business boom if the sharks were to turn savage? It's all very well saying these sharks are environmentally friendly and only eat wee fish. That's boring; it's blood that the public want to see. I inched my head carefully, scanning for Stuart's return.

15 Panic and paranoia rose with my air bubbles as I caught a blurry glimpse of my foe curving around on the other side of the tunnel with a lazy flick of its tail. This sand tiger shark was nine feet long and approaching about six feet in front and above me. My lungs began to pipe the *Jaws* theme up in my throat.

16 A few images from the film looped in my head before it arrived: Robert Shaw desperately kicking at the munching mouth of the great white shark, before disappearing inside; the severed leg dropping to the bottom of the boating pond, a tumbling head, and Roy Schneider up on a sinking flag pole, taking aim and screaming, "Smile, you son of a . . . " BOOM!

17 And then it was before me in direct contrast to the celluloid nightmares of Hollywood. There was no evil eye staring me out, no prowling movement or even any interest. Instead it swam by like a bored fridge. Just then, water began to fill my mask obscuring the view. Once I had cleared it my foe-turned-distant-friend was disappearing into the distance. Suddenly I felt a hand on my shoulder marking Stuart's return with photographer Gavin Anderson.

18 Gavin seemed confident and relaxed. "If we want to get a picture of you with a shark you're going to have to get quite close so I can blast it with the flash and get the shot."

19 "That won't annoy it?" I worried.

20 "What?"

21 "The shark, you won't annoy it?"

22 "It'll be fine," he said, shaking his head and administering a friendly pat.

23 Thirty feet down he fiddled with his camera while occasionally giving the OK signal—thumb and first finger in a circle while the remaining three stick up in the air. I responded, though the mouthpiece hid the manic grins I made.

24 To recap on the sunken scene, I was kneeling on the bottom with my tank to the tunnel. Stuart was stationed protectively to my left side while Gavin hung about on the right, itching to shoot. I felt like bad bait—only crowds of cod, bass and flounder flocked towards me.

25 Ten or twelve of them mobbed round my mask, occasionally touching the glass before fleeing. Then I remembered sharks eat fish and suddenly felt like jam in a swiss roll at a kids' tea party. But they wouldn't leave. Just then Gavin got excited which could mean only one thing— the return of the floating fridge.

26 Earlier, while changing, we had rehearsed how I would tilt my head backwards so that my face and the shark's would fit inside the same picture. But I couldn't do it. I didn't want to. I slightly tilted my head and noticed the soft underbelly breeze above me, close enough to touch. This was real, not an image from a movie.

27 The finest moment of a memorable dive was when we slowly rose to the surface as a giant skate flapped past on one side while a sand tiger shark browsed by below me. The chance of such an encounter in the open seas would be as slim as my chances of survival without Stuart's reassuring presence and training.

28 Breaking the surface and wrenching out the mouthpiece, I swore, and swore, and swore. Swearing is sometimes more descriptive for the indescribable as the words come charged with more impact. I had swum with sharks. Childhood fears and attractions had been relived when I touched another world. I simply wanted to return.

[*END OF PASSAGE*]

[BLANK PAGE]

G

0860/404

Total Mark	

NATIONAL
QUALIFICATIONS
2000

TUESDAY, 16 MAY
1.00 PM – 1.50 PM

**ENGLISH
STANDARD GRADE**
General Level
Reading
Questions

Fill in these boxes and read what is printed below.

Full name of centre

Town

Forename(s)

Surname

Date of birth
Day Month Year   Scottish candidate number   Number of seat

**NB Before leaving the examination room you must give this booklet to the invigilator.
If you do not, you may lose all the marks for this paper.**

SCOTTISH
QUALIFICATIONS
AUTHORITY

MCB 0860/404 6/68020

©

QUESTIONS

Write your answers in the spaces provided.

Look at Paragraphs 1 to 3.

1. **Write down** an expression the writer uses which suggests that he was having difficulty getting dressed for diving.

_____

2
0

2. **Write down** an expression he uses to show how he feels about the sharks.

_____

2
0

3. (*a*) What reason was the writer given for believing that the sharks wouldn't want to eat him?

_____

2
0

(*b*) Explain fully why the writer was not reassured by this reason.

_____

_____

_____

2
1
0

4. "I didn't feel like a flounder, but given time . . . "

Why do you think the writer **deliberately** chose not to complete this sentence?

_____

_____

2
1
0

Look at Paragraphs 4 and 5.

5. "In the next chamber was the world's largest underwater safari . . ."

Show how the writer continues this idea throughout Paragraph 4.

_____

_____

2
1
0

DO NOT
WRITE IN
THIS
MARGIN

6. Explain fully how The Preacher got its name.

_____

_____

2
1
0

Look at Paragraphs 6 to 9.

7. Explain the difference between a wet suit and a dry suit by completing the following sentences. **Use your own words as far as possible.**

(i) A wet suit keeps you warm by _____

_____

_____

2
1
0

(ii) A dry suit keeps you warm by _____

_____

_____

2
1
0

8. Explain clearly why the writer had to struggle to keep his balance at the bottom of the small tank.

_____

_____

2
1
0

Look at Paragraphs 10 to 12.

9. Once he was in the main safari tank, the writer noticed various aspects of the fish and their world. Give **three** of them.

(i) _____

(ii) _____

(iii) _____

2
1
0

10. Apart from the loss of balance, what other problem did the writer experience, and how did he overcome it?

_____

_____

2
1
0

Look at Paragraphs 13 and 14.

11. Why do you think the writer has chosen the word "flooded" to describe how his memories returned?

_____

_____

2
1
0

12. The writer notices a little four-year-old watching him.

(a) Explain clearly why the writer worried about this at first.

_____

_____

2
1
0

(b) Why did he change his mind?

_____

_____

2
1
0

13. ". . . it's blood that the public want to see." (Paragraph 14)

What evidence does the writer give that savagery is good for business at Deep Sea World?

_____

_____

2
1
0

Look at Paragraphs 15 to 22.

14. What effects did the "blurry glimpse" (Paragraph 15) of the shark have on the writer?

_____

_____

2
1
0

15. ". . . it swam by like a bored fridge." (Paragraph 17)

Explain how effective you find this comparison.

_____

_____

_____

2
1
0

16. **Write down** an expression from this section which shows that the writer's attitude towards the shark had started to change.

_____

2
0

17. Explain clearly what worried the writer about having his picture taken with a shark.

_____

_____

2
1
0

Look at Paragraphs 23 to 26.

18. What expression tells us that the writer was still worried even though he responded to the photographer's OK signal?

_____

2
0

19. **In your own words**, explain clearly why the writer felt "like jam in a swiss roll at a kids' tea party". (Paragraph 25)

_____

_____

2
1
0

Look at Paragraphs 27 and 28.

20. Explain fully why the writer felt that the finest moment was "when we slowly rose to the surface". (Paragraph 27)

_____

_____

2
1
0

21. **In your own words**, explain why the writer thinks that swearing can sometimes be more effective than using ordinary words.

_____

_____

2
1
0

[Turn over for Question 22 on _Page six_

Think about the passage as a whole.

22.   "I had swum with sharks." (Paragraph 28)

    (*a*)   What evidence is there earlier in the article that he had had a childhood interest
        in sharks?

_____

_____

    (*b*)   From your reading of the article, how do you think the writer felt about sharks
        or his experience of swimming with them **compared with his expectations**?

_____

_____

_____

[END OF QUESTION PAPER]

G

0860/403

NATIONAL
QUALIFICATIONS
2001

MONDAY, 14 MAY
1.00 PM – 1.50 PM

ENGLISH
STANDARD GRADE
General Level
Reading
Text

Read carefully the passage overleaf. It will help if you read it twice. When you have done so,
answer the questions. Use the spaces provided in the Question/Answer booklet.

The Appeal of

1   All the junk in Scotland meets your befuddled gaze: thousands of unwanted gifts, the "wee something" for Christmas and the "I saw this and thought of you" for your birthday (how you wish they hadn't); then there are the holiday souvenirs. In short, all the stuff with which we tend to clutter our lives and our cupboards has somehow ended up in one place, awkwardly arranged on a vast number of folding tables.

2   Behind them, all kinds of people are perched on the tailgates of a variety of vehicles. Is this some bizarre store for recycled rubbish? Well, in a way it is. In other words, you have found yourself in the middle of your first car boot sale. They can be found most weekends in summer, and sometimes in winter too, in villages, towns and cities throughout the country. Sometimes they are held on an occasional basis—a charity or other organisation will hire a hall or a school playground, advertise in the local press and rent out pitches at £5 or £10 for the day. Other sales are held every Saturday or Sunday on more permanent sites.

3   Women seem to outnumber men behind the essential tables: although men often come to help to set up, they retire shyly for most of the day and return in the late afternoon to pack up the left-overs. Curiously enough, there are as many male customers as female: all human life wanders by.

4   There goes a plump medallion man who will tell you—his unhappily captive audience—a succession of unfunny and wildly politically incorrect jokes at which you will laugh, lamely, and hope he goes away.

5   There goes a succession of polite elderly gentlemen, clean and smart in their car coats; they will go off happily clutching boxes of your ancient gardening tools to which their wives will most surely object, but who are you to spoil their fun?

6   There is, just occasionally, a serious side to all this, which may affect the buyer rather than the genuine seller. Car boot sales can provide a certain amount of cover for less honest traders and it is as well to bear this in mind if you are offered a more than average bargain. Where, for instance, did those big canisters of cleaning fluid designated "Janitorial Supplies" originate? And what about those suspiciously home-made looking video cassettes of all the latest movies? Trading Standards Officers sometimes visit boot sales to keep a lookout for fakes. Police

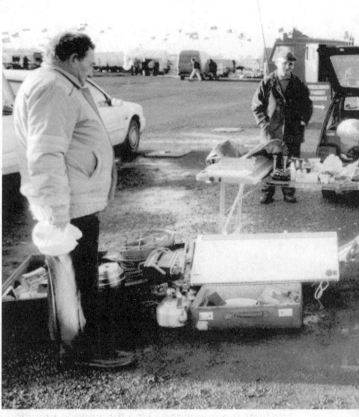

Never underestimate what will sell. Old console games or market for all

occasionally find stolen goods lurking among the junk. Customs and Excise may be investigating those suspiciously cheap cigarettes and Environmental Health Officers may even be wondering whether that delicious home-made tablet has been concocted with due regard to public health.

7   But on the whole, say the police, they have little trouble with car boot sales. Most are legitimate and harmless: ordinary punters offloading bric-a-brac onto other ordinary punters. To a Martian hovering up there we must all look like nothing so much as a colony of ants, struggling to carry off various large and cumbersome objects, a table here, a suitcase there . . .

8   So if you fancy trying a boot sale, just for the fun of it, here are a few ground rules for participating in this most rewarding game.

9   Go as a buyer first, if you can. Have a good look around. Some pitches are better than others. Some are closer to the loos. Some are on windy corners and some may be right next to the little roundabout that plays the same four-bar tune all day long.

10   Go early, if you are selling. Many car boot sales that advertise an opening time of 10 am are being set up by seven or eight in the morning.

Car Boot Sales

videos will disappear as if by magic and there is a ready
kinds of gadgets.

11 Beware of the antique dealers. They will surround your table at this early hour like wild dogs around a carcase, fingering your Aunty Annie's floral teapot with its dripping spout and trying to decide if they are getting the bargain of the century at £1·50 including chipped lid. Remember the Antiques Roadshow. Remember that daft little pottery owl that fetched thousands.

12 Invest in a cheap wallpapering table. You can sell out of the boot of your car, but if you have as much junk to get rid of as most of us do, you will need more space than the average hatchback can supply. Take a secure container for your money—preferably a money belt so that you can keep your takings safely about your person. Don't leave handbags lying around; car boot sales are hunting grounds for purse snatchers. By the same token it's wise to take a friend. Then you have someone to mind the stall while you take time out to browse around the neighbouring stalls.

13 Don't sell old electrical goods: they can be dangerous, and you can be in trouble with the law for doing so.

14 Take lots of food and drink with you: sandwiches, chocolate bars, flasks of tea and coffee, cans of soft drinks. You will be amazed

at how hungry and thirsty you will get standing around all day and there is little point in blowing your takings on hamburgers although the smell will certainly drive you wild. Wear comfortable shoes and remember to take warm clothes, even in summer. Remember to plan for rain. This is Scotland after all, and you will probably get cold and wet.

15 Don't overprice your goods, but never underestimate what will sell either. The truth is that people will buy almost anything if the price is right. Old Playstation games, or genuine second-hand videos, will disappear as if by magic. Even more surprisingly, so will large, rickety (and empty) wooden boxes, elderly baseball caps that were given free with something ten years ago, shabby plastic dinosaurs that have been in many an imaginary battle and a pile of kitchen gadgets such as the tattie peeling machine that always took ages to wash afterwards, the expensive plastic containers with ill-fitting lids and the pancake mixer that liberally sprinkled you with batter every time you tried to use it. Just lay it out and somebody will come along wanting to buy it.

16 Above all, don't expect to make any fortunes. What you will do is recycle a truly astonishing amount of junk, give an amazing amount of pleasure to all kinds of people, observe all human life wandering past your table, and come home with a modest profit. That's if you can stop yourself from filling your car boot with other people's junk before you go home.

17 After all there's a little collection of pressed glass over there that is so irresistible, and the old hand-knitted Shetland shawl that nobody seems to have spotted, and isn't that a genuine stone hot-water bottle lurking among the rubbish . . . ?

Adapted from an article in "The Scotsman" by Catherine Czerkawska.

[END OF PASSAGE]

[BLANK PAGE]

G

Total
Mark

0860/404

NATIONAL
QUALIFICATIONS
2001

MONDAY, 14 MAY
1.00 PM – 1.50 PM

ENGLISH
STANDARD GRADE
General Level
Reading
Questions

Fill in these boxes and read what is printed below.

Full name of centre

Town

Forename(s)

Surname

Date of birth
Day Month Year   Scottish candidate number   Number of seat

**NB Before leaving the examination room you must give this booklet to the invigilator.
If you do not, you may lose all the marks for this paper.**

SCOTTISH
QUALIFICATIONS
AUTHORITY

QUESTIONS

Write your answers in the spaces provided.

Look at Paragraphs 1 and 2.

1. "All the junk in Scotland meets your befuddled gaze"

   How does the writer continue the idea of "junk" in the first two paragraphs?

   _____

   _____

   2
1
0

2. **Write down an expression** from Paragraph 2 which shows that the writer thinks this "junk" makes a **strange collection**.

   _____

   2
1
0

3. Explain the **differences** between the two types of car boot sale described in Paragraph 2.

   (i) _____

   _____

   2
1
0

   (ii) _____

   _____

   2
1
0

Look at Paragraphs 3 to 5.

4. (a) When it comes to selling, women "seem to outnumber men".

   Write down the expression the writer uses to suggest why the men don't do the selling.

   _____

   _____

   2
0

   (b) When it comes to buying, there are "as many male customers as female".

   What is the writer's reaction to this? Answer in your own words.

   2
0

5. (*a*) The writer gives two examples of "human life" wandering by.
In your own words, explain as fully as you can why the writer:

    (i) disapproves of the "plump medallion man" _____

_____

_____

2
1
0

    (ii) might sympathise with the "succession of polite elderly gentlemen".

_____

_____

2
1
0

(*b*) Explain fully what the writer gains by using the expression "There goes . . ." to introduce these two examples.

_____

_____

2
1
0

Look at Paragraphs 6 and 7.

6. Explain **in your own words** what the writer means by the "serious side" of car boot sales.

_____

_____

2
1
0

7. (*a*) What do each of the following organisations look for at car boot sales?

    (i) Trading Standards _____

    (ii) Police _____

    (iii) Customs and Excise _____

2
1
0

(*b*) Explain what concerns the Environmental Health Officers might have about any food on sale.

_____

_____

2
1
0

8. **Write down** an expression which shows that there are very few concerns about the "serious side" of car boot sales.

_____

2

0

Look at Paragraphs 8 to 14.

9. In Paragraph 8 the writer introduces the idea of giving practical advice.

How does the sentence construction at the beginning of Paragraphs 9 to 14 help to show this?

_____

2

0

10. (a) **Write down** the simile or comparison which describes how the antique dealers behave.

_____

2

0

(b) Explain what is appropriate about this comparison.

_____

2

1

0

11. From Paragraph 12, **explain in your own words** why:

(a) you should "invest in a cheap wallpapering table".

_____

_____

2

1

0

(b) you would be "wise to take a friend".

_____

_____

2

1

0

Look at Paragraph 15.

12. " . . . people will buy almost anything . . ."

The writer gives several examples to prove this statement.

Choose any **two** (APART FROM GAMES AND VIDEOS).

In each case explain why the writer thinks it is surprising that anyone should buy them.

(i) _____

_____

2
1
0

(ii) _____

_____

2
1
0

Look at Paragraphs 16 and 17.

13. The writer believes several benefits can be gained from car boot sales. **In your own words** describe two of them.

(i) _____

(ii) _____

2
1
0

14. What do you think the writer is suggesting by her descriptions of the items in Paragraph 17?

_____

2
1
0

15. Why does the writer use ellipsis (. . .) at the end of the final sentence?

_____

2
0

Think about the passage as a whole.

16. Look at the photograph which accompanies the article.

Explain how it shows examples of the following:

(i) the writer's advice being taken _____

_____

(ii) the writer's advice being ignored _____

_____

2
1
0

[Turn over for Question 17 on *Page six*

17. Tick (✓) **one** of the following expressions which you think **best** describes the writer's purpose in this article.

Explain your choice by detailed reference to the text.

to provide information ☐   to entertain ☐

to be thought-provoking ☐

_____

_____

_____

_____

2
1
0

[END OF QUESTION PAPER]

0860/105

SCOTTISH CERTIFICATE OF EDUCATION 1996	TUESDAY, 7 MAY 2.30 PM – 3.20 PM	**ENGLISH STANDARD GRADE** Credit Level Reading Text

Read carefully the passage overleaf. It will help if you read it twice. When you have done so, answer the questions. Use the spaces provided in the Question/Answer booklet.

SCOTTISH EXAMINATION BOARD

This passage is an extract from a novel set in Russia in 1905. It describes a childhood experience of an encounter with death.

1   Asya pulled on her coat and boots, closed the pantry door and slipped away before anyone saw her disappear. Her breath streamed through her muffler and rose up into the birch branches above her head. The icicles on the eaves shed a steady stream of drops into the piled snowbanks on either side of the path; clumps of snow slid off the branches of the firs and subsided to the ground with a hiss; the uppermost branches of the birches sighed and cracked in the wind. She skipped down the hundred and twenty-six wooden steps to the boathouse singing to herself.

2   Inside the boathouse, slivers of winter light streamed through the gaps between the plank walls and sliced her body into planes of illumination and darkness. The racing craft gleamed on the rafters above her head and the motor launch, suspended above its river berth by twin ropes, swayed slightly to and fro, making a dry, creaking sound.

3   She climbed down the boathouse ladder and tested the ice with her boot. Then she pushed open the great wooden doors and stepped out into the fierce light of the silver river. In the far distance, she could just make out the thin line of the opposite shore. Father had once crossed the river on snowshoes. She would too. She would astonish them all. She walked along, sucking her mitten.

4   She glanced back at the house, where she had left her brother Lapin playing snakes and ladders with Nanny Saunders, but the village of Marino had vanished in the mist. Whenever she stopped pushing her boots through the slushy ice, she could hear the river roaring beneath her feet. Soon the ice would begin to heave and crack, and the air would fill with a groaning sound as if the whole earth were in pain. Then the river would throw off its mantle and jagged chunks would begin to shift and then bob past the dock. She loved it when the frozen world began to move, when the torrent of life reclaimed the river for its own. Marino would awaken from its sleep. The boatman would sand and revarnish the hull of the motor launch and grease the oarlocks on the rowing boat. As soon as the ice was off the water, Father would dive naked from the boathouse and roar when he surfaced, throwing the hair out of his eyes.

5   She slopped through the slush, thinking of Spring. By the time she reached the middle of the river, the mist had enveloped her. The boathouse behind her was gone, and the long, smudged line of her water-filled steps trailed away into nothingness. The pencil line of the opposite shore had disappeared. She stood still and listened. A faint sound. A scythe being drawn against a sharpening-stone. A blade being honed on something hard. She turned around, sucking her mitten, trying to figure out which direction the sound was coming from. Blades scything, blades hissing, coming closer. Where had she heard that sound before? Then she knew. It was a skater, out there in the mist, coming towards her. No one she knew. They were all inside. She could hear his breathing now, his body at full stretch, his blades slicing into the river's skin. She stood still, waiting for him, unafraid and alone. The veil of mist burst apart, the vast white figure hurtled past her and the ice beneath her feet gave way. She subsided into a dark hole of water, clutching at the jagged rim, while the river seized hold of her and tore her boots from her feet. The river roared in her ears and liquid warmth—like that of a nursery bath—rose through her body and she let herself be swept away.

6   Then faces were leaning over her, and hands were busy about her, rubbing her limbs frantically, wiping the tears from their faces with such a look of desolation that she wanted to ask what the matter was, but could not speak, only stare up at them from the warm watery place where she had gone. She was borne aloft and carried upwards, wrapped up tight, as if in swaddling. From where she lay in their arms, she stared up into the black, naked branches of trees lit by the pink sky of dusk. Beneath her and behind her she could hear the steady crunch of boots in the snow and a woman weeping. She could not move her head or see where she was being taken.

7   She opened her eyes and saw that Praskoviya was bathing her face with a cloth. How much better it had been out on the river. How much better it had been in the warm, watery place. How beautiful their tears had seemed when she could only lie there and watch them fall. How painful they were now, when you could reach up and wipe them from Praskoviya's face.

8   "My child! You have come back from the dead! The Lord be praised."

9   Why was she talking of death? There was no death on the river, only warmth suffusing her body and the certainty of having seen a great vision.

10   "Whatever possessed you, my dearest?" Her mother's voice, close by, gentle, anguished.

11   Her eyes shut tight, Asya heard herself say in a shrill voice: "I saw a skater. A great skater. Out there. On the ice."

12   She looked up. They were all crowded around her bed: Father, Mother, her brother Lapin, Praskoviya, but she could tell from their faces that no one had seen what she had seen or heard what she had heard. All the remaining years of her life, she remembered that moment: when she discovered the abyss of unknowing that separated her from those she loved.

13   She looked about her. Where was Nanny Saunders?

14   Her father laid his hand upon hers.

15   "The groom is accompanying her to the station."

16   "But why?"

17   "She has been dismissed for letting you out of her sight."

18   All the way back to England? In the winter? She could imagine the black carriage trotting through the dark woods, Nanny Saunders with her boxes in the back seat.

19   "Don't cry, child, don't cry."

20   But there was no stopping these tears, mixed with grief and rage. Much later, when she had learned what life was like, she remembered this as the moment when she discovered injustice, and the possibility that a father could be responsible for it.

21   "It was not Nanny's fault. You told me you crossed the river. It's not her fault! Call her back!"

22   Dr Feldman tried to force her head back onto the pillow. "You mustn't, child, you mustn't . . ."

[Turn over

23   "I cannot call her back. My mind is made up," said Father in that reasonable tone of voice that she knew issued from a will stronger than her own.

24   "But you told me you crossed the river on snowshoes."

25   "Did I, child?" His long face with its neatly trimmed beard, smelling of wintergreen, was close to hers. She could not bear to think that he had forgotten, that he took his words to her so lightly. She turned away from her father and began to cry.

Adapted from *Asya* by Michael Ignatieff

[END OF PASSAGE]

Presenting Centre No.	Subject No. 0860	Level	Paper No.	Group No.	Marker's No.

C

Total Mark

0860/106

SCOTTISH
CERTIFICATE OF
EDUCATION
1996

TUESDAY, 7 MAY
2.30 PM – 3.20 PM

**ENGLISH
STANDARD GRADE**
Credit Level
Reading
Questions

Fill in these boxes and read what is printed below.

Full name of school or college

Town

First name and initials

Surname

Date of birth
Day Month Year

Candidate number

Number of seat

**NB Before leaving the examination room you must give this booklet to the invigilator.
If you do not, you may lose all the marks for this paper.**

SCOTTISH
EXAMINATION
BOARD

Marks

QUESTIONS

Write your answers in the spaces provided.

Look at Paragraph 1.

1. **Write down** an expression which suggests that Asya went out secretly.

_____   2 ■ 0

2. **In your own words**, give **two** pieces of evidence that there was a thaw.   2 1 0

   (i)   _____

   (ii) _____

3. (*a*) What kind of mood did Asya seem to be in?

   _____   2 ■ 0

   (*b*) Write down **two** separate words which the writer uses to convey the impression of her mood.

   2 1 0

Look at Paragraph 2.

4. **Using your own words**, describe the effect of the winter light on Asya's appearance.

   _____

   _____   2 1 0

PAGE
TOTAL

Marks

Look at Paragraph 3.

5. Asya "stepped out into the fierce light of the silver river".

   (a) Explain clearly why the light would seem "fierce".

   _____

   _____   2 | 1 | 0

   (b) Give **two** reasons why you think the writer chose the word "silver" to describe
   the river.   2 | 1 | 0

       (i) _____

       (ii) _____

6. How does the writer convey the idea that Asya was determined, yet seemed nervous,
   about crossing the river?   2 | 1 | 0

   Determined _____

   _____

   Nervous _____

   _____

Look at Paragraphs 4 and 5.

7. **In your own words**, describe the **three** things Asya looked forward to once the ice
   had gone.   2 | 1 | 0

       (i)   _____

       (ii) _____

       (iii) _____

8. "She slopped through the slush . . ."

   How is the writer's choice of words effective in describing Asya walking across the
   river?

   _____

   _____   2 | 1 | 0

PAGE
TOTAL

Marks

9. ". . . the mist had enveloped her."

   Explain **in your own words** how the writer develops this idea in the two sentences which follow.

   _____

   _____

   _____   2 1 0

10. "She stood still and listened."

    (*a*) What **two** features of structure does the writer use to convey the sound Asya hears?   2 1 0

       (i)   _____

       (ii) _____

    (*b*) Why does he choose to write in this way?

       _____

       _____   2 1 0

11. (*a*) What impression of the skater is created by the writer's description?

       _____   2 ■ 0

    (*b*) **Quote** an expression to support your answer to question 11(*a*).

       _____   2 ■ 0

12. Why does the expression ". . . his blades slicing into the river's skin" suggest a sense of danger?

    _____

    _____   2 1 0

PAGE TOTAL

Marks

13. ". . . liquid warmth—"

    "—like that of a nursery bath—"

    (a) Given the context, what is surprising about these two expressions? | 2 | 1 | 0 |

        (i) _____

        (ii) _____

    (b) Which expressions in **Paragraph 6** continue these unusual ideas? | 2 | 1 | 0 |

        (i) _____

        (ii) _____

14. The writer describes the river as if it were a living thing.

    (a) Give an example of this.

        _____ | 2 | ■ | 0 |

    (b) Comment on the effect of your chosen example.

        _____

        _____ | 2 | 1 | 0 |

Look at Paragraph 6.

15. Why might the people's faces have had "such a look of desolation"?

    _____ | 2 | ■ | 0 |

Look at Paragraphs 7 to 9.

16. "My child! You have come back from the dead! The Lord be praised."

    Explain why Asya was puzzled when she heard this.

    _____

    _____ | 2 | 1 | 0 |

PAGE
TOTAL

Marks

Look at Paragraphs 10 to 12.

17. **In your own words**, explain what Asya remembered about that moment "all the remaining years of her life".

_____

_____   2 ■ 0

Look at Paragraphs 13 to 25.

18. Explain clearly why Asya felt it was "not Nanny's fault".

_____

_____   2 1 0

19. In these final paragraphs of the passage, Asya learned things about her father which disappointed her.

Describe **two** of them as fully as you can.

(i) _____

_____   2 1 0

(ii) _____

_____   2 1 0

Think about the passage as a whole.

20. There are several important moments for Asya in this extract.

(a) Which **one** do you think affected her most?

_____

_____   2 ■ 0

(b) **By close reference to the passage**, explain your choice as fully as you can.

_____

_____

_____

_____   2 1 0

[END OF QUESTION PAPER]

PAGE
TOTAL

FOR OFFICIAL USE

p2	
p3	
p4	
p5	
p6	
TOTAL MARK	

FOR OFFICIAL USE

[BLANK PAGE]

0860/105

SCOTTISH
CERTIFICATE OF
EDUCATION
1997

WEDNESDAY, 7 MAY
2.30 PM – 3.20 PM

ENGLISH
STANDARD GRADE
Credit Level
Reading
Text

Read carefully the passage overleaf. It will help if you read it twice. When you have done so, answer the questions. Use the spaces provided in the Question/Answer booklet.

SCOTTISH
QUALIFICATIONS
AUTHORITY

©

MCB 0860/105 6/43010

That old white magic

The ancient pagan religion of witchcraft (or "Wicca") has not always been perceived as evil.

However the craft has suffered from a prolonged spell of bad publicity.

The devil's daughters: James VI took witchcraft so seriously that he and blamed a coven in North Berwick, shown in this contemporary

1   **P**ITY the poor witch on Hallowe'en as she climbs aboard her trusty broomstick and, with familiar cat riding pillion, whizzes off to the *Samhain Sabbat*. She has had an awfully bad press over the years.

2   In popular folklore, she is the warty old crone who dances naked around a bonfire on the nights of the eight annual sabbats and then, as dawn breaks, smears herself with "flying ointment" and jets back home for a glass of toadslime and a hot bath.

3   She is the old dear forever depicted as a somewhat unlovely woman dressed casually in black and wearing an ungainly pointy bunnet. Let's face it, looking like that she would stick out a mile in your average supermarket.

4   Our perceptions of the witchcraft cult are deeply and subconsciously rooted: we may scoff at childhood terrors, but how many of us would be entirely happy walking through a graveyard at night? We may have

forgotten our fear of the dark and the supernatural, but we have also seen *Nightmare on Elm Street*.

5   The witch has come to symbolise primordial fears lurking just beneath the surface in all of us: Freddie, *Night of the Living Dead*, and the bogeyman rolled into one. The three witches in *Macbeth*, prancing and cackling around their cauldron, provide the accepted clichés on witch behaviour and taste:

> *Eye of newt, and toe of frog*
> *Wool of bat, and tongue of dog*
> *Adder's fork, and blind-worm's*
> *sting*
> *Lizard's leg and howlet's wing*

6   However "tongue of dog" and "adder's fork" are plants—the former used as the basis for a contemporary cough medicine. Shakespeare, living as he was at the beginning of the great witch persecutions, perhaps was not above pulling a few legs. Alas, the *Macbeth* witches have merely served to reinforce prejudice, rather than cast illumination.

7   So does the witch deserve her poor image? As she frolics cold and naked, invoking the names of the old

gods — Cernunnos and the moon goddess Diana — might it not occur to her that over the centuries she has had a pretty raw deal? In many ways, she would be quite right.

8   It is probable that the Wiccan creed goes back to the dawn of religious belief, when cave dwellers peered out and saw wonder in the rhythm of the changing seasons. Early cave drawings from across Europe — and elsewhere — show remarkable similarities, particularly in their depiction of a horned god.

9   Early witchcraft was probably no more than a primitive attempt to make sense of the unknown. It is likely that the Wiccan horned god was an earlier version of the Greek god Pan. So how come this religion became associated with hubble bubble, toil and trouble?

10   The answer was an unhappy alliance between the spread of Christianity and social upheaval. In the so-called Dark Ages witchcraft was considered no more than a misdemeanour, warranting the equivalent of community service; yet in the "enlightened" Renaissance,

# of Wicca's world

wrote a treatise against it, personally supervised the torture of witches, woodcut, for a storm at sea in which he was caught in 1590.

the fires burned across Europe (except in England where witchcraft was a hanging offence).

1 During the 15th century, witchcraft and Christianity had co-existed; the church recognising that older pagan cults of beliefs could not easily be repressed — particularly in backward rural communities where survival was often a matter of luck, and old superstitions die hard.

2 The book *Malleus Maleficarum* (*Hammer of the Witches*), published in 1486, was the trigger for a change in attitude which gave the Church the big stick it needed to beat non-conformity and heresy; in the process, it sparked a Europe-wide holocaust against Jew and witch alike. (In some areas of Europe, the *Malleus* was used specifically against Jews; indeed, in Hungary a first offender found guilty of witchcraft was made to stand for a day in a public place wearing a Jew's hat.)

3 In England, where judicial torture was illegal (except for some treasonable crimes), the witch persecution was mild compared to elsewhere in Europe. In Scotland, however, judicial torture was practised with uncommon zeal; for example, the use of pennywinkis which crushed the toes and fingers, or the leg screw which splintered the shin bone. Small wonder that the victim confessed and, having done so, named her accomplices. The beauty of the witch craze was that it was self-fulfilling; the more brightly the witch fires burned, the more victims were then found.

14 In Scotland, the first witch law in 1563 prescribed the death penalty for all witches, "good" and "bad". Until then the Church had made a distinction between harmless superstitious belief and what might now be termed black magic — a distinction that modern witches see as fundamental to an understanding of their beliefs.

15 Thereafter, all witchcraft was evil — James VI of Scotland also abolished the distinction in England on his accession to the throne there — and the black-hatted old crone as modern stereotype begins to emerge. One aspect of that stereotype is true: it was women who bore the brunt of it. One estimate suggests one hundred women died for every man condemned for witchcraft.

16 The simple explanation is that local wisewomen offered an easy target. Since time immemorial, these local worthies had acted as doctor, vet, pharmacist and midwife, offering an accumulation of folk wisdom handed down over the generations. During the years of persecution, it became a job with few prospects when anyone with a score to settle could denounce the wisewoman as a witch.

17 The persecution may be behind us but the witches live on. Estimates of their numbers are understandably hard to find but the upsurge in the number of (white witch) covens reflects both a disenchantment with modern technological life and a desire to return to more primitive roots — the religious equivalent of herbal healthcare.

18 Witchcraft echoes still abound in petty superstition — for example, the number 13 (the number of witches in a coven), or throwing salt over our left shoulder. And how many people know that the children's rhyme *Who Killed Cock Robin?* is a reference to the now-defunct English Wiccan ritual of sacrificing small birds in the apple orchards?

19 Nowadays your average witch is likely to be called Harry or Morag and live in a nice wee house in the country or a council flat in town. On the way to the *Samhain Sabbat*, he/she is also likely to go by bus or car, rather than risk it on the carpet shampooer (technology again, you see). And no, she won't take a short-cut home through the graveyard. Like you and I, she would be too frightened.

Adapted from an article in *The Scotsman* by Charles Laidlaw

[*END OF PASSAGE*]

[BLANK PAGE]

Total Mark

0860/106

SCOTTISH
CERTIFICATE OF
EDUCATION
1997

WEDNESDAY, 7 MAY
2.30 PM – 3.20 PM

ENGLISH
STANDARD GRADE
Credit Level
Reading
Questions

Marks

QUESTIONS

Write your answers in the spaces provided.

Look at Paragraphs 1 to 3.

1. **In your own words**, give **three** pieces of information which are popularly believed about witches.

    (i) _____

    (ii) _____

    (iii) _____

    2 1 0

Look at Paragraphs 4 to 6.

2. "Our perceptions of the witchcraft cult are deeply and subconsciously rooted".

    (*a*) What **two** examples does the writer give in Paragraph 4 to support this idea?

    _____

    _____

    2 1 0

    (*b*) Which expression in Paragraph 5 contains a similar idea to this quotation?

    _____

    2 1 0

3. In what way does the quotation from *Macbeth* show that Shakespeare was "pulling a few legs"?

    _____

    _____

    2 1 0

4. Explain **in your own words** any **one** belief the writer has about the *Macbeth* witches.

    _____

    _____

    2 1 0

PAGE
TOTAL

Marks

Look at Paragraph 7.

5. In what way can Paragraph 7 be regarded as a link of the ideas within the article?

_____

_____   2 | 1 | 0

Look at Paragraphs 8 and 9.

6. **Quote** an expression which shows that the writer is not certain of the facts.

_____   2 | ■ | 0

7. **In your own words**, explain what the writer believes was the purpose of early witchcraft.

_____

_____   2 | 1 | 0

8. What is the difference in tone between the last sentence of Paragraph 9 and the rest of these two paragraphs?

_____

_____   2 | ■ | 0

Look at Paragraphs 10 to 12.

9. Explain **in your own words** how you can tell that witchcraft wasn't badly thought of in the Dark Ages.

_____

_____   2 | 1 | 0

10. Why has the writer used inverted commas round the word "enlightened"?

_____

_____   2 | 1 | 0

PAGE
TOTAL

Marks

11. **In your own words**, explain clearly why the Christian Church accepted the existence of witchcraft.

_____

_____ | 2 | 1 | 0 |

12. Describe **in your own words one** effect of the publication of the *Malleus Maleficarum*.

_____

_____ | 2 | 1 | 0 |

Look at Paragraph 13.

13. Explain **in your own words** what, according to the writer, was the "beauty of the witch craze".

_____

_____ | 2 | 1 | 0 |

Look at Paragraph 14.

14. What difference did the 1563 law make to the Church's dealings with "good" and "bad" witches?

_____

_____ | 2 | 1 | 0 |

15. **Quote** an expression which shows that the distinction between "good" and "bad" is important to modern witches.

_____ | 2 | ■ | 0 |

PAGE
TOTAL

Marks

Look at Paragraphs 15 and 16.

16. ". . . the black-hatted old crone as modern stereotype"

    Explain **in your own words** what evidence there is that "one aspect of that stereotype is true".

    _____

    _____   2 | 1 | 0

17. Why were wisewomen often "an easy target"?

    _____

    _____   2 | 1 | 0

Look at Paragraph 17.

18. **In your own words**, state what the writer knows about the number of present-day witches.

    _____

    _____   2 | 1 | 0

19. The writer gives two reasons for people's interest in joining witches' covens. **In your own words**, explain each as fully as you can.

    (i) _____

    _____   2 | 1 | 0

    (ii) _____

    _____   2 | 1 | 0

Look at Paragraph 18.

20. **Quote** a word or expression which shows that small birds are no longer sacrificed in Wiccan rituals.

    _____   2 | ■ | 0

[Turn over for Questions 21 to 23 on *Page six*

PAGE
TOTAL

Marks

Look at Paragraph 19.

21. (a) What impression does the writer give of the average modern witch?

    _____   2 ■ 0

    (b) Give **two** examples of how the writer conveys this impression.   2 1 0

        (i) _____

        (ii) _____

Think about the passage as a whole.

22. The tone of this article is at times humorous.

    (a) **Quote one** example of the writer's use of humour.

        _____

        _____   2 ■ 0

    (b) Explain fully how the humorous effect is achieved.

        _____

        _____

        _____   2 1 0

23. (a) What do you consider the writer's attitude to witches to be?

        _____   2 1 0

    (b) By detailed reference to the content of the article, give a reason for your answer to (a).

        _____

        _____

        _____   2 1 0

[END OF QUESTION PAPER]

PAGE
TOTAL

FOR OFFICIAL USE

p2 ☐

p3 ☐

p4 ☐

p5 ☐

p6 ☐

TOTAL
MARK ☐

[BLANK PAGE]

0860/105

SCOTTISH
CERTIFICATE OF
EDUCATION
1998

WEDNESDAY, 6 MAY
2.30 PM – 3.20 PM

**ENGLISH
STANDARD GRADE**
Credit Level
Reading
Text

Read carefully the passage overleaf. It will help if you read it twice. When you have done so, answer the questions. Use the spaces provided in the Question/Answer booklet.

In this extract the writer gives his impressions of an area of Montana called the Badlands

1   *Mauvaises terres*. The first missionary explorers had given the place this name, a translation of the Plains Indian term meaning something like hard-to-travel country, for its daunting walls and pinnacles and buttresses of eroded sandstone and sheer clay. Where I was now, in Fallon County, Montana, close to the North Dakota state line, the Badlands were getting better. A horseback rider wouldn't have too much difficulty getting past the blisters and eruptions that scarred the prairie here. But the land was still bad enough to put one in mind of Neil Armstrong and the rest of the Apollo astronauts: dusty, cratered, its green turning to sere yellow under the June sun.

2   Breasting the regular swells of land, on a red dirt road as true as a line of longitude, the car was like a boat at sea. The ocean was hardly more solitary than this empty country, where in forty miles or so I hadn't seen another vehicle. A warm westerly blew over the prairie, making waves, and when I wound down the window I heard it growl in the dry grass like surf. For gulls, there were killdeer plovers, crying out their name as they wheeled and skidded on the wind. *Keel-dee-a, Keel-dee-a.* The surface of the land was as busy as a rough sea—it broke in sandstone outcrops, low buttes, ragged bluffs, hollow combers of bleached clay, and was fissured with waterless creek beds, ash-white, littered with boulders. Brown cows nibbled at their shadows on the open range.

3   The road ahead tapered to infinity, in stages. Hill led to hill led to hill, and at each summit the road abruptly shrank to half its width, then half its width again, until it became a hairline crack in the land, then a faint wobble in the haze, then nothing. From out of the nothing now came a speck. It disappeared. It resurfaced as a smudge, then as a fist-sized cloud. A while passed. Finally, on the nearest of the hilltops, a full-scale dust-storm burst into view. The storm enveloped a low-slung pick-up truck, which slowed and came to a standstill beside the car, open window to open window.

4   "Run out of gas?"

5   "No"—I waved the remains of a hideous sandwich. "Just having lunch."

6   The driver wore a stetson, once white, which in age had taken on the colour, and some of the texture, of a ripe Gorgonzola cheese. Behind his head, a big-calibre rifle was parked in a gun-rack. I asked the man if he was out hunting, for earlier in the morning I'd seen herds of pronghorn antelope; they had bounded away from the car on spindly legs, the white signal-flashes on their rumps telegraphing *Danger!* to the rest. But no, he was on his way into town to go to the store. Around here, men wore guns as part of their everyday uniform, packing Winchesters to match their broad-brimmed hats and high-heeled boots. While the women I had seen were dressed in nineties clothes, nearly all the men appeared to have stepped off the set of a period Western. Their quaint costume gave even the most arthritic an air of strutting boyishness that must have been a trial to their elderly wives.

7   "Missed a big snake back there by the crick." He didn't look at me as he spoke, but stared fixedly ahead, with the wrinkled long-distance gaze that solo yachtsmen, forever searching for landfall, eventually acquire.

8   "He was a real beauty. I put him at six feet or better. It's a shame I didn't get him—I could have used the rattle off of that fellow . . ."

9   With a blunt-fingered hand the size of a dinner plate, he raked through the usual flotsam of business cards, receipts, spent ball-points and candy wrappings that had collected in the fold between the windshield and the dash. "Some of my roadkills," he said. Half a dozen snake rattles, like whelk shells, lay bunched in his palm.

10   "Looks like you have a nice little hobby there."

11   "It beats getting bit."

12   He seemed in no particular hurry to be on his way, and so I told him where I came from, and he told me where he came from. His folks had homesteaded about eight miles over in *that* direction—and he wagged his hat brim southwards across a treeless vista of withered grass, pink shale and tufty sage. They'd lost their place back in the thirties. "The dirty thirties." Now he was on his wife's folks' old place, a dozen miles up the road. He had eleven sections up there.

13   A section is a square mile. "That's quite a chunk of Montana. What do you farm?"

14   "Mostly cattle. We grow hay. And a section and a half is wheat, some years, when we get the moisture for it."

15   "And it pays?"

16   "One year we make quite a profit, and the next year we go twice as deep as that in the hole. That's about the way it goes, round here."

17   "That's the way farmers like to say it goes just about everywhere, isn't it?"

18   We sat on for several minutes in an amiable silence punctuated by the cries of the killdeer and the faulty muffler of the pick-up. Then the man said, "Nice visiting with you," and eased forward. In the rear-view mirror I watched his storm of dust sink behind the brow of a hill.

19   In the nineteenth century, when ships under sail crossed paths in mid-ocean, they "spoke" to each other with signal flags; then, if sea conditions were right, they hove to, lowered boats, and the two captains, each seated in his gig, would have a "gam", exchanging news as they bobbed on the wavetops. In *Moby-Dick*, Melville devoted a chapter to the custom, which was evidently still alive and well on this ocean-like stretch of land. It was so empty that two strangers could feel they had a common bond simply because they were encircled by the same horizon. Here it was a hard and fast rule for drivers to slow down and salute anyone else whom they met on the road, and it was considered a courtesy to stop and say howdy. Fresh from the city, I was dazzled by the antique good manners of the Badlands.

Adapted from *Bad Land* by Jonathan Raban

[END OF PASSAGE]

[BLANK PAGE]

Total Mark

0860/106

SCOTTISH
CERTIFICATE OF
EDUCATION
1998

WEDNESDAY, 6 MAY
2.30 PM – 3.20 PM

ENGLISH
STANDARD GRADE
Credit Level
Reading
Questions

Fill in these boxes and read what is printed below.

Full name of school or college

Town

First name and initials

Surname

Date of birth
Day Month Year

Candidate number

Number of seat

NB Before leaving the examination room you must give this booklet to the invigilator. If you do not, you may lose all the marks for this paper.

SCOTTISH
QUALIFICATIONS
AUTHORITY

Marks

QUESTIONS

Write your answers in the spaces provided.

Look at Paragraph 1.

1. (a) Who were the first people to see the Badlands, according to this paragraph?

   _____   2 ■ 0

   (b) Explain clearly how you know.

   _____

   _____   2 1 0

2. Explain clearly what made the Badlands "hard-to-travel" before reaching Fallon County.

   _____

   _____

   _____   2 1 0

3. ". . . blisters and eruptions that scarred the prairie . . ."
   Explain what this expression adds to the writer's description of the area in Fallon County.

   _____

   _____

   _____   2 1 0

Look at Paragraph 2.

4. **Quote** an expression that emphasises the straightness of the road the writer was travelling and explain why it is effective.

   _____

   _____

   _____   2 1 0

PAGE
TOTAL

Marks

5. (*a*) In the first sentence of this paragraph, what is it that makes the car seem "like a boat at sea"?

_____

_____   2 1 0

(*b*) Show how the writer continues this idea in the rest of the paragraph.

_____

_____

_____

_____   2 1 0

Look at Paragraph 3.

6. "The road . . . tapered to infinity . . ."

Explain how the CONTENT and STRUCTURE of the **second sentence** in Paragraph 3 help to make the meaning of this expression clear.

CONTENT   _____

_____

_____

_____   2 1 0

STRUCTURE _____

_____

_____   2 1 0

PAGE
TOTAL

Marks

7. Explain how you are made to "see" the approach of the pick-up truck as the writer saw it.

_____

_____

_____

_____   2 | 1 | 0

Look at Paragraphs 4 to 6.

8. What **two** things led the writer to ask the driver of the truck if he was hunting?   2 | 1 | 0

   (i) _____

   (ii) _____

9. (*a*) What **three** aspects of the **men's costumes** reminded the writer of "the set of a period Western"?   2 | 1 | 0

   (i)   _____

   (ii)   _____

   (iii) _____

   (*b*) **In your own words,** explain what **effect** was created by these costumes.

   _____

   _____

   _____   2 | 1 | 0

   (*c*) Why do you think this effect "must have been a trial" to their wives?

   _____

   _____

   _____   2 | 1 | 0

PAGE
TOTAL

Marks

Look at Paragraphs 7 to 11.

10. What "nice little hobby" did the truck driver appear to have?

_____

_____   2   1   0

11. **Quote two** expressions from this section that continue the comparison between the prairie and the ocean.   2   1   0

    (i) _____

    (ii) _____

Look at Paragraphs 12 to 17.

12. The truck-driver is a homesteader or farmer.

Why might this area seem an unlikely place for a farm?

_____

_____   2   1   0

13. **In your own words**, explain why the truck driver did **not** grow wheat every year.

_____

_____   2   ■   0

14. Explain, **in your own words**, what it is that farmers complain of "just about everywhere".

_____

_____   2   1   0

[Turn over for Questions 15 to 18 on *Page six*

PAGE
TOTAL

Marks

Look at Paragraphs 18 and 19.

15. **Quote** an expression that suggests that, despite being strangers, the two men were quite comfortable in each other's company.

_____   2 ■ 0

16. What can you infer about the behaviour of people who live **in the city**? Explain how you arrived at your answer.

_____

_____

_____   2 1 0

17. Explain fully why the writer refers to the novel *Moby-Dick* in the final paragraph.

_____

_____

_____   2 1 0

Think about the passage as a whole.

18. Jonathan Raban's main purpose in this piece of writing is to share his experience of the Badlands.

    What feature of the writing most helps him to achieve this purpose?

    Refer to at least one example of the feature you choose.

_____

_____

_____

_____   2 1 0

[END OF QUESTION PAPER]

PAGE
TOTAL

FOR OFFICIAL USE

p2 ☐

p3 ☐

p4 ☐

p5 ☐

p6 ☐

TOTAL
MARK ☐

[BLANK PAGE]

0860/105

SCOTTISH
CERTIFICATE OF
EDUCATION
1999

FRIDAY, 30 APRIL
2.30 PM – 3.20 PM

ENGLISH
STANDARD GRADE
Credit Level
Reading
Text

Read carefully the passage overleaf. It will help if you read it twice. When you have done so, answer the questions. Use the spaces provided in the Question/Answer booklet.

Patrick Chamoiseau remembers his childhood on the Caribbean island of Martinique.

1   Fort-de-France had not yet declared war on the rats. Along with the crabs, they infested the crumbling sidewalks and canals of the city. They haunted the gullies. They scoured the basements; they emerged from the nocturnal refuse. Absorbed with his spiders, his cockroaches and his dragonflies, the little boy didn't notice them right away. A few squeaks here and there. A fleeting shadow in the canal. But during one of his moments of stillness on the roof of the kitchens, he came upon a fabulous spectacle.

2   At about one in the afternoon, Fort-de-France became lethargic, with fewer pedestrians and fewer horns. People sought refuge in the shade to eat. The dust of this urban desert began to flutter. Behind the house, on the roof of the kitchens, a shadow offered a cool haven for the little boy. On Saturday afternoons the languor deepened. Finally, the house creaked under the weight of silence and the little boy was free to do nothing, to be still. It was on a day like this when a squeak lifted him from his inner emptiness, calling him to the edge of the roof. That's when he saw the rats, down in the courtyard. Five or six, yes, there they were—scourers searching for crumbs, tub climbers, tightrope artists on the edge of buckets, disappearing into the kitchens and reappearing just as fast. Very young rats and very old rats. Others, fearful, emerged from the covered canal only to pounce on a titbit of food.

3   Among the rats there was one that was older than the others: slower, more wary, but more powerful and more cunning. He ventured into the open only in conditions of complete security, against a backdrop of pure silence. Not until the floorboards of the house stopped moving, and the town shut down and gave in to the dust, did the old rat risk his shadow beneath the vertical heel of the sun. He was massive, and stitched up with scars; he had lost an ear, a piece of his tail, and perhaps also some part of himself which made him no longer merely a rat. He was so experienced it was terrifying: his heart didn't leap at every puff of wind, but his finely tuned ear and acute eye told him when to disappear instantly. He had no habits, never passed the same spot twice and never retreated in the same manner. This was the rat the boy chose as his very first victim.

4   A strange relationship developed. The boy found a piece of string and created a slip-knot which he laid out in the courtyard. In the middle, he set down a piece of sausage. And with the knot wedged in place, the string in his fist, he sat lookout on the roof.

5   The idea was to lasso the vicious old rat. But the animal must have disliked sausage or else the sight of the lasso cast him into a strategic sadness which kept him in his hole, philosophizing about dark rat affairs. Whatever the case, he never showed up. It was always a younger, stupider rat who ventured into the slip-knot and lunged for the sausage. The boy pulled with all his might—he must have pulled a thousand times. But eventually he had to accept the impossibility of catching a rat with this sausage-lasso set-up. The knot would close around itself, and the impatient boy would haul up nothing but a dangling string.

6   His next contraption was a basin weighted down by a rock. A piece of wood connected to an invisible string held it in the air. The old rat (he never turned up) was supposed to venture underneath in order to collect the bait. Those who did risk it raced off with the sausage as if conscious of the trap. At other, rarer, times they

fled empty-mouthed. After a while, not a single one came. There was the flaming gourd, the infernal jar, the superglue, the rubber band, the guillotine-knife, the poison syrup, the terrifying scissor of doom . . . But even this arsenal of small cruelties was not enough to snare the slightest hint of rat. Too late, he learned that he had to suppress his own smell from the traps, and could never reuse a bait. The rats would avoid any dubious windfalls that lay invitingly within tooth's reach. The boy took some time to understand that, in fact, rats were intelligent.

7   One day the old rat spotted him. Standing on the edge of the tub, he furtively glanced his way, then pursued his quest. Two inhuman orbs of opaque blackness served as his eyes. For a split second these eyes brushed over him, and, in a certain sense, scorned him. Never again did the old rat, even though he knew the boy was watching, grant him a second glance. He modified his routes and always remained far from the overhang of the roof where the boy—changing his tactics, trying to be selective—was perched, rock in hand, directly above the bait on the ground, waiting to crush the Old Man's back.

8   Hours of lookout were required, the rock held in his outstretched hand above the void: lying on the tin, watching with only one eye, hoping for silence, breathing in calmness, turning to rust in order to melt into the roof, praying for the old rat to approach, ignoring the other rats that dared to nibble the bait.

9   Towards the end the boy's stiffened arms would drop the vengeful rock on any frenzied latecomers; but even these avoided being crushed, with leaps that became increasingly leisurely. Their losses beneath the far-too-slow moving stone never amounted to more than a snippet of tail, a tuft of hair. Around these measly trophies the boy organized pagan ceremonies.

10   The old rat disappeared sometimes, not to be seen for several weeks. The little boy supposed him dead. He imagined secret cemeteries visited by night. He imagined the streets covered with all these exhausted rats, who knew their way around poison and who, suddenly hearing some obscure call, would set out to dig a grave with their last tooth. He imagined his ageing adversary, a rat isolated by his years: so much intelligence, such cunning, such caution, so much genius—all ending in dirty dereliction, with no address other than death and forgetting. So the boy arranged funerals for him on tiny cars. A box of matches served as a coffin. The procession travelled the hallway and ended in a liturgy he improvised himself, in rat language. A burial concluded this ceremony—in a hole gouged in the wall near the stairs. The boy would go away melancholy, missing his old friend, until one day he would see him reappear. Then, rather than rejoicing, he would dash off to invent some atrocity capable of finishing him off, this time for real.

11   He watched him grow old. It was nothing: a stiffness in the back, a misshapen silhouette, the constant shaking of an ear. He was horrified to see him take risks, react slowly. He caught the Old Man nibbling things he had scoffed at before; and often he seemed immobile, distracted in a senile kind of way. The boy watched him fall apart. A feeling of pity rose up in him: he felt no desire to kill, only the horror of a benign commiseration. He often had the impression that if he came down from the roof, the Old Man would wait for him and allow himself to be touched.

[Turn over

12   One day, the Old Man limped towards the bait, right under the rock which the boy still brandished, out of habit, from the heights of his lookout. He advanced with a kind of blind,—or desperate, or absent-minded-faith, something like a suicidal impulse, or the sense that he had little to lose. He stepped into the trap and began chewing like a cockroach on the bait.

13   The stone did not crush his skull: it had become the keystone of a cathedral of pity in the child, who wept.

Adapted from Carol Volk's translation of *Childhood* by Patrick Chamoiseau

[END OF PASSAGE]

Total Mark

0860/106

SCOTTISH
CERTIFICATE OF
EDUCATION
1999

FRIDAY, 30 APRIL
2.30 PM – 3.20 PM

ENGLISH
STANDARD GRADE
Credit Level
Reading
Questions

Fill in these boxes and read what is printed below.

Full name of school or college

Town

First name and initials

Surname

Date of birth
Day Month Year

Candidate number

Number of seat

NB Before leaving the examination room you must give this booklet to the invigilator. If you do not, you may lose all the marks for this paper.

SCOTTISH
QUALIFICATIONS
AUTHORITY

Marks

QUESTIONS

Write your answers in the spaces provided.

Look at Paragraphs 1 and 2.

1. (*a*) Explain how the writer, in **Paragraph 1**, emphasises the **number** of rats inhabiting the city of Fort-de-France.

   _____

   _____

   _____   2 | 1 | 0

   (*b*) Given that there were so many rats around, explain **in your own words** why the little boy had not noticed them.

   _____

   _____   2 | 1 | 0

2. ". . . Fort-de-France became lethargic . . ." (Paragraph 2)

   (*a*) What does this mean and why do you think it happened?

   _____

   _____

   _____   2 | 1 | 0

   (*b*) **Quote** an expression used later in Paragraph 2 that suggests a similar idea.

   _____   2 | ■ | 0

PAGE
TOTAL

Marks

3. In Paragraph 1, what the boy saw is called a "fabulous spectacle".
   Use the information in **Paragraph 2** to answer.

   (*a*) What **exactly** did the little boy see?

   _____

   _____   2 | 1 | 0

   (*b*) Why does he refer to it as a "a fabulous spectacle"?

   _____

   _____

   _____

   _____   2 | 1 | 0

Look at Paragraph 3.

4. (*a*) **In your own words, explain** in what ways the old rat was superior to the others.

   _____

   _____   2 | 1 | 0

   (*b*) **Quote** the expression that suggests that the old rat had almost supernatural powers.

   _____   2 | 1 | 0

5. What do you find effective about the **last sentence** of this paragraph? Why?

   _____

   _____

   _____   2 | 1 | 0

[Turn over

PAGE
TOTAL

Marks

Look at Paragraphs 4 and 5.

6. (a) When using his "sausage-lasso set-up", why did the boy fail to catch,

   (i) the old rat?

   _____

   _____

   (ii) any of the younger rats?

   _____

   _____   2 1 0

   (b) **Quote** the expression which suggests that the boy persisted with this method for some time.

   _____   2 ■ 0

Look at Paragraphs 6 to 9.

7. What made the boy think that the rats knew the basin "contraption" was a trap?

   _____

   _____   2 ■ 0

8. **In your own words**, explain why his "arsenal of small cruelties" failed to "snare the slightest hint of rat".

   _____

   _____   2 1 0

9. What conclusion did the boy eventually reach?

   _____

   _____   2 ■ 0

PAGE
TOTAL

Marks

10. "One day the old rat spotted him." (Paragraph 7)

    (*a*)   **Quote** the expression that suggests the **lack of concern** in the way the old rat looked at the boy.

_____   2 ■ 0

    (*b*)   **In your own words**, what suggests the old rat was, however, nervous of the boy's presence?

_____

_____   2 1 0

11. ". . . was perched, rock in hand . . ." (Paragraph 7)

What does the writer's use of the word "perched" add to the image created that a simpler word like "sitting" would not?

_____

_____

_____   2 1 0

12. Explain what is unusual about the expression "measly trophies".

_____

_____   2 1 0

Look at Paragraph 10.

13. The writer chooses to begin three sentences in a row with the words "He imagined". What does he gain by doing so?

_____

_____   2 1 0

[Turn over

PAGE
TOTAL

Marks

14. **In your own words**, what is surprising about the boy's reaction to the old rat's reappearance?

_____

_____   **2 1 0**

Look at Paragraphs 11, 12 and 13.

15. "The boy watched him fall apart." (Paragraph 11)

In your own words, list **three** things that betrayed the fact that the old rat was beginning to fail.   **2 1 0**

   (i)   _____

   (ii) _____

   (iii) _____

16. (*a*) **Quote** the expression from **Paragraph 12** which suggests that the boy did not have much confidence in his latest trap.

   _____   **2 ■ 0**

   (*b*) ". . . like a cockroach . . ." (Paragraph 12)

   What does this expression suggest about the boy's attitude to the rat's action and why does it do so?

   _____

   _____

   _____   **2 1 0**

PAGE
TOTAL

Marks

Think about the passage as a whole.

17. Which **one** of the following words **best** describes the boy's attitude to the old rat throughout the passage? Tick (✓) the appropriate box.

CONTEMPTUOUS	
OBSESSIVE	
FEARFUL	
DISMISSIVE	

Justify your selection, **using evidence from the text**.

_____

_____

_____   2 1 0

18. What do you find effective about the **last paragraph** as an ending to the passage as a whole? Support your answer with **evidence from the text**.

_____

_____

_____

_____   2 1 0

[END OF QUESTION PAPER]

PAGE
TOTAL

FOR OFFICIAL USE

p2 ☐

p3 ☐

p4 ☐

p5 ☐

p6 ☐

p7 ☐

TOTAL
MARK ☐

0860/405

NATIONAL
QUALIFICATIONS
2000

TUESDAY, 16 MAY
2.30 PM – 3.20 PM

ENGLISH
STANDARD GRADE
Credit Level
Reading
Text

Read carefully the passage overleaf. It will help if you read it twice. When you have done so, answer the questions. Use the spaces provided in the Question/Answer booklet.

A writer reflects on the changes which have taken place in a coastal area of southern Ireland.

1   You can walk along the strand all the way from Ardmore to the derelict one-storey Georgian house on the cliff. You pass Ballyquin on the way, a little cove that has a car park now. The sand is smooth and damp, here and there marbled with grey, or dusty dry, depending on whether you choose to walk by the sea or closer to the cliffs. There are shrimps and anemones in the rock pools, and green slithery seaweed as you pass the rocky places by. The cliffs are clay, easy game for the encroaching winter waves. Washed timber and plastic bottles are the flotsam of the shingle.

2   A woman pushes a bicycle, the buckets that hang from its handlebars heavy with seafood from the rocks. A horse and cart carries gravel or seaweed back to Ballyquin. In the nineteen thirties this strand was always empty, except on the rare days when a solitary figure could be seen, suddenly there out of nowhere, clambering down the cliff-face. Clothes were weighed down with a stone and then he ran naked to the sea.

3   Inland a little way, not always visible from the strand, is Ballyquin House, four-square and architecturally simple, cream-washed when the O'Reillys lived there. Mrs O'Reilly, a widow, attired always in black, was a woman whose unobtrusive presence called for, but did not demand, respect. All the old decencies were in the woman that Mrs O'Reilly was: you hardly had to look at her to know she would rather not live at all than live dubiously, in some mean-spirited way. Her two children, Biddy and Henry, were in their early twenties. Her brother, a silent man who kept his hat on, worked the farm. An old uncle—known as Blood-an'-Ouns because he so often used the expression—got drunk in Ardmore every Easter but otherwise did not touch a drop.

4   Henry O'Reilly was known locally as the laziest man in Ireland, but in my childhood opinion he was also the nicest. Red-haired and already becoming bulky, he took me with him on the cart to the creamery and on the way back we would stop at a crossroads half-and-half—a shop that was a grocery as well as a public house. He had a bottle of stout himself, and bought me a lemonade and biscuits. He would settle his elbows on the counter, exchanging whatever news there was with the woman who served us. "Give the boy another mineral," he'd say, and he'd order another packet of biscuits for me, or a Cadbury's bar. Eventually the horse would take us slowly on, lingering through the sunshine, Henry O'Reilly having a nap, the reins in my charge. Most of the day it took, to go to the creamery and back.

5   Henry O'Reilly made me an aeroplane, nailing together a few scraps of wood, which he then painted white. He showed me how to snare a rabbit and how to shoot one. When I was eight or so I weeded a field of turnips with him, a task that didn't require much energy because we stopped whenever a new story began, and Henry O'Reilly went in for stories. At twelve o'clock we returned to the farmhouse and sat down in the kitchen to a meal of potatoes, which were tumbled out on to a newspaper in the centre of the table.

6   The O'Reillys' land stretched right to the cliff edge, but the O'Reillys rarely ventured on to the strand, as country people who live by the sea so often don't. There were cows to milk, and feed to be boiled for the hens, and crops to be harvested, the churns of milk delivered. The front door of the house was never opened, the rooms on either side of it and the bedrooms above only entered when dusting took place.

7   There is a glen where the strand ends, separating the land that was once the O'Reillys' from woods that have become dense. And there, much closer to the cliff edge than the O'Reillys', is the derelict house. The woods stretch for miles behind it and somewhere in the middle of them lived a man with rheumy eyes called Paddy Lyndon. In a tumbled-down outbuilding there was an old motor-car with brass headlamps—one of the first, Paddy Lyndon averred, that had taken to the roads in Ireland. "Are you sober, Paddy?" Henry O'Reilly would always greet Paddy Lyndon when they met, an enquiry that received no response.

8   Glencairn House the derelict place was called when first I knew it fifty years ago. It was owned then by an Englishman who'd left Ireland during the Troubles and only rarely returned—a Mr Fuge who'd built a dream house, not knowing that dreams are not to be trusted. "As good a man as ever stood on two feet," Paddy Lyndon said. "A man that never owed a debt." Through the cracks of the efficiently boarded windows nothing could be distinguished in the darkness that kept the rooms' secrets. A briar rose trailed through a patch of garden, gone as wild as the surrounding gorse. I liked the mystery of this good Englishman who'd left his property in Paddy Lyndon's charge, who only stayed for twenty minutes when he came back. "There's stories about Fuge I could tell you," Henry O'Reilly said, but he never did because he never got round to making them up.

9   But it is the sea, not houses or people, that dominates the strand. To the sea, and the sand and rocks that receive it, belong the images you carry with you when you pass on to the woody slopes of the glen, and the barley fields. The waves call the tune of the place, in a murmur or a passionate crescendo. There's salt on the inland air, and seagulls strut the furrows.

10   Jellyfish float in when they're in a mood for it. Once in a while there's a trawler on the horizon. The sea on the turn's the best, the sand left perfect or waiting to be doused. It's easier to skim pebbles over the water when it's unruffled—as it was the time I nearly drowned, causing panic one hot afternoon.

11   Two generations on, the shells are as they've always been; so are the paw-prints of a dog. The dog has a branch of brown seaweed trailing from its jaws, and takes no notice when he's called. People nod as they pass, or say hullo. Children build castles and watch them being washed away, old men paddle. A primus stove splutters. It's out of the question that a naked figure will run into the sea.

12   Still no one lives in the derelict house. The boards that once so curtly covered the windows, a kind of packing case around the house, have fallen away. You can see the rooms now, but if ever there was furniture all of it has gone. The wall beside the avenue has collapsed.

[Turn over

13   The O'Reillys' farmhouse is different too. Years ago Biddy made her way to Chicago, Henry married into Ardmore. Mrs O'Reilly and her brother, the old uncle too, are long since dead. The house is no longer in the family, the land is differently farmed.

14   There is no nostalgia here, only remembered facts—and the point that passing time has made: the strand is still the strand, taking change and another set of customs in its stride, as people and houses cannot. While you walk its length, there is something comforting in that.

Adapted from *Excursions in the Real World* by William Trevor

[END OF PASSAGE]

C

Total
Mark

0860/406

NATIONAL
QUALIFICATIONS
2000

TUESDAY, 16 MAY
2.30 PM – 3.20 PM

**ENGLISH
STANDARD GRADE**
Credit Level
Reading
Questions

Fill in these boxes and read what is printed below.

Full name of centre

Town

Forename(s)

Surname

Date of birth
  Day Month Year

Scottish candidate number

Number of seat

**NB Before leaving the examination room you must give this booklet to the invigilator.
If you do not, you may lose all the marks for this paper.**

SCOTTISH
QUALIFICATIONS
AUTHORITY

©

MCB 0860/406 6/3/43020

QUESTIONS

Write your answers in the spaces provided.

Look at Paragraphs 1 and 2.

1. In what way is the sand different at either edge of the strand?

    _____   2

    _____   1

                                                                      0

2. Explain fully why the cliffs are described as "easy game" for the waves in winter.

    _____   2

    _____   1

                                                                      0

3. (a) **In your own words**, explain the difference between the strand today and the
         strand in the nineteen thirties.

         _____   2

                                                                      1

         _____   0

    (b) What has been provided in the area which might have contributed to this
         difference?

                                                                      2

         _____   0

Official SQA Past Papers

121

DO NOT
WRITE IN
THIS
MARGIN

Look at Paragraphs 3 to 5.

4. **Quote** an expression which indicates that Mrs O'Reilly was not a very noticeable woman.

_____

2
0

5. What was one of the "old decencies" which the writer felt was obvious in Mrs O'Reilly?

Answer in your own words.

_____

_____

2
1
0

6. The writer uses the dash (—) in the last sentence of Paragraph 3 and the second sentence of Paragraph 4.

Explain their different function in each case.

(i) **Paragraph 3** _____

_____

2
0

(ii) **Paragraph 4** _____

_____

2
0

7. Give **three** pieces of evidence which suggest why Henry O'Reilly would be:

(a) **known locally** as the laziest man in Ireland.

(i) _____

(ii) _____

(iii) _____

2
1
0

(b) **thought by the writer** to be the nicest man in Ireland.

(i) _____

(ii) _____

(iii) _____

2
1
0

[Turn over

Look at Paragraphs 6 to 8.

8. **In your own words**, explain **fully** why the O'Reillys, like other country people, "rarely ventured on to the strand".

_____

_____ **2**
1
_____ **0**

9. "Glencairn House the derelict place was called . . ."

Give **two** examples from Paragraphs 7 and 8 which support this description.

(i) _____ **2**
1
(ii) _____ **0**

10. Explain **in your own words** why the writer describes Mr Fuge as "not knowing that dreams are not to be trusted".

_____

_____ **2**
1
_____ **0**

11. Why did Paddy Lyndon think Mr Fuge was a good man?

_____ **2**
0

12. Why might it seem strange that Mr Fuge had "left his property in Paddy Lyndon's charge"?

_____

_____ **2**
1
_____ **0**

Look at Paragraphs 9 to 11.

13. "But it is the sea, not houses or people, that dominates the strand."

   (a) Explain how this sentence is an effective link between the earlier part of the
       passage (Paragraphs 3 to 8) and the rest of Paragraphs 9 to 11.

   _____

   _____   2

                                                                               1

   _____   0

   (b) Explain how the **structure** of the second sentence of Paragraph 9 ("To the sea
       . . . barley fields.") emphasises the importance of the sea.

   _____   2

                                                                               1

   _____   0

   (c) Quote **two examples** of the writer's **word-choice** in the rest of Paragraph 9
       which continue to emphasise the dominance of the sea.

   (i) _____   2

                                                                               1

   (ii) _____   0

14. What **two** contrasting impressions of the sea does the writer convey in Paragraph 10?

   _____   2

                                                                               1

   _____   0

15. Why do you think the writer **repeats** the reference to "a naked figure" at this point?

   _____   2

                                                                               1

   _____   0

[Turn over for Questions 16 and 17 on *Page six*

Look at Paragraphs 12 to 14.

16. (*a*) What evidence does the writer give in Paragraphs 12 and 13 to illustrate the changes in **both** people and houses?

_____

_____

_____

2
1
0

    (*b*) **In your own words**, describe the feelings he expresses about the strand in the last paragraph.

_____

_____

2
1
0

Think about the passage as a whole.

17. The writer's purpose in this article is to **describe** and **reflect upon** the strand, its surroundings and people.

Several features of his writing help him to achieve his purpose—for example word-choice, selective detail, figures of speech, structure etc.

Select **two** features and, by referring to an example of each, show how they help to make his writing effective.

    (i) _____

_____

_____

2
1
0

    (ii) _____

_____

_____

2
1
0

[*END OF QUESTION PAPER*]

0860/405

NATIONAL
QUALIFICATIONS
2001

MONDAY, 14 MAY
2.30 PM – 3.20 PM

ENGLISH
STANDARD GRADE
Credit Level
Reading
Text

Read carefully the passage overleaf. It will help if you read it twice. When you have done so, answer the questions. Use the spaces provided in the Question/Answer booklet.

SCOTTISH
QUALIFICATIONS
AUTHORITY

In this extract the narrator reflects on the first visit of an aunt and cousin.

1   They didn't come to England till 1962. It was the "*n*"-th year of preparations for a visit that always, in the end, failed to happen.

2   I'd just arrived home for autumn half-term and at first I didn't believe what I was told—that their plane had touched down at the airport—and I wasn't convinced till I saw for myself the black Humber Hawk taxi come swinging up the drive, axles creaking, carrying its two passengers in the back, one swathed in furs.

3   "It's your cousin," my mother told me unnecessarily, nervous beside me on the top step as we made a little reception committee with my father for our guests none of us had ever seen.

4   The driver opened the back door of the taxi and my "aunt", as we referred to her—really my mother's aunt's daughter—divested herself of the travelling rugs. She hazarded a foot out on to the gravel—in a pointy crocodile shoe—as if she were testing the atmosphere. She emerged dressed in a waisted black cashmere overcoat with a fur collar and strange scalloped black kid-skin gloves like hawking gauntlets.

5   I saw my mother noting again the black stiletto-heeled shoes with their red piping. The face we'd never seen was hidden under a broad-brimmed black felt hat, which I felt none of the women *we* knew in our closed circle would have had the courage to put on their heads.

6   "Hi!" my aunt greeted us in a surprisingly light, sprightly voice, unpinning the furs across her shoulders.

7   A shadow moved behind her in the car. Behind them both the driver was lifting half a dozen assorted white suitcases out of the boot. My mother drew in her breath.

8   "It's so cold!" my aunt called to us from under her hat. "Brr, I can't take it like this!"

9   Then she smiled—at the three of us, each in turn—quite charmingly.

10   My mother relaxed, realising our guest was only being eccentric, not insulting.

11   "Well I hope you'll be warm *here*," my mother told her by way of introduction, with just a little "tone" in her voice.

12   I could see better now. Beneath her discreetly black coat my aunt had very long, slender, shapely legs. Behind her, her son—my cousin Walter—ventured unsurely into the hall.

13   "Unfortunately," my mother addressed the face under the hat, "you've come at the very coldest season."

14   "Oh, I know I'll be very warm here, I can tell already," my aunt assured her with another toothpaste advertisement smile, throwing her furs on to a chair like a film star. "Very comfortable. I've so wanted to see you all, you can't imagine."

15   My mother smiled—cautiously—and my father closed the door.

16   "Do come and have some tea, both of you," he said.

17   He was forever at a loss with guests to Oakdene, my father: now for some reason a smile was starting to break on his reserved banker's "business" face my mother and I were so used to living with.

18   I examined my cousin surreptitiously while I helped my father carry the cases to the foot of the staircase—while *he* just stood there, doing nothing. He was odd-looking, I saw. He had a triangular-shaped face with a bony chin, and he was bloodlessly, alarmingly pale. He stood with his shoulders hunched; very arched eyebrows and flat ears set close against his head added to the pixie-ness of his appearance. What made me think him odder still was his not seeming to match at all with his elegant (and, from what I could see, pretty) mother. (How ugly must his father be, I wondered, to correct the balance of heredity?) He was several inches shorter than I was, although I knew we were the same age (eleven, if the year was 1962). His height—or his lack of height—was another disappointment, and also his thinness. I'd expected he would look stolid, and assertive, and the very picture of glowing health. Instead the eyes in his pale face flitted among us, like a prying spinster's, missing nothing.

19   "Did you have a nice flight?" my mother asked, with controlled politeness. "I can't remember where . . ."

20   "Oh, we've been everywhere! Everywhere!" my aunt explained, pausing at the hatstand to remove her wide-brimmed hat. She seemed to take off twenty years with it and suddenly I felt they were a generation apart, she and my mother. My aunt pulled at her hair—becomingly blonde (dyed, I think it must have been) and smartly cut—with the tips of her fingers. In her black crocodile shoes and with her black lizard bag and the long kid gloves tucked into the pockets of her coat, she looked very expensive. I was utterly fascinated.

21   "Paris. Como. Rome." She crossed them off on those creamed, manicured fingers with their scarlet nails. (She was making little perfume trails whenever she moved.) "Where else, now? Antibes, of course. And we saw a little bit of Switzerland. That *was* cold!"

22   She walked ahead of us into the sitting-room and made for the fireplace and the crackling log fire.

23   "Capri. That was just heaven. And Naples, of course."

24   My mother watched her from the hall. "Of course," she repeated, just to herself, under her breath.

25   Their visit to us was bad timing. We were having a very cold snap, and in another week—when our guests would have gone—it would be November, then December after that, with Christmas fir trees for sale in the village shops. We were to be their last stop before they flew home. I suppose we were a family obligation. Or—were we really something else, a different kind of invitation to their travellers' curiosity . . . ?

26   In our sitting-room my aunt seemed very exotic, and rather theatrical: not at all like my staid "county" mother with her scrubbed grouse-moor complexion. For "housewives", how unalike they seemed! On a scale of prettiness my aunt might have scored seven marks out of ten: she certainly "made the most of what she had"—as my mother would say of certain women she didn't quite approve of, because (another of her expressions) they "tried too hard".

[Turn over

27   When my aunt took off her coat she was wearing a canary silk suit underneath, and my mother looked most uncomfortable in the other big wing-chair, pulling her tweed skirt over her knees and tugging at the pearls round her throat. My cousin Walter sat, not where he was invited to, but on a hard-bottomed shield-back chair from where he could observe all our different posturings with his range of vision clear and unimpeded.

28   My aunt burst the seal on a pack of cigarettes and leaned forward in her chair to catch the flame from my father's lighter. I saw my mother taking a suddenly critical view of the situation. Her face was set in a way I wasn't unfamiliar with.

29   "You'll have some tea, Stella?"

30   My aunt nodded through the thick blue fog of cigarette smoke. I noticed how speedily her eyes were racing round our sitting-room, as Walter's had done earlier, recording our possessions.

31   Like my mother I was already starting to feel not at all at my ease: almost—silly to say—like a stranger here in my own home.

Adapted from a short story by Ronald Frame

[END OF PASSAGE]

C

Total
Mark

0860/406

NATIONAL
QUALIFICATIONS
2001

MONDAY, 14 MAY
2.30 PM – 3.20 PM

ENGLISH
STANDARD GRADE
Credit Level
Reading
Questions

Fill in these boxes and read what is printed below.

Full name of centre

Town

Forename(s)

Surname

Date of birth
Day Month Year

Scottish candidate number

Number of seat

**NB Before leaving the examination room you must give this booklet to the invigilator.
If you do not, you may lose all the marks for this paper.**

SCOTTISH
QUALIFICATIONS
AUTHORITY
©

QUESTIONS

Write your answers in the spaces provided.

Look at Paragraphs 1 to 3.

1. **In your own words**, explain fully why the narrator at first didn't believe that "their plane had touched down at the airport".

   _____

   _____

       2
       1
       0

2. What finally convinced him it was true?

   _____

   _____

       2
       1
       0

3. (a) Why was the narrator's mother "nervous"?

   _____

   _____

       2
       1
       0

   (b) What evidence is there of her nervousness?

   _____

       2
       0

Look at Paragraphs 4 and 5.

4. (a) What impression of the aunt do you get from the writer's choice of the words "divested", "hazarded" and "emerged" to describe her movements?

   _____

       2
       0

   (b) What is added to this impression by his description of what she was wearing?

   _____

       2
       0

5. What is the function of the dashes (—) used in Paragraph 4?

   _____

       2
       0

Look at Paragraphs 6 to 15.

6. "My mother drew in her breath." (Paragraph 7)

   (*a*) What does this tell you about her feelings?

   _____

   2
   0

   (*b*) What caused her to react this way?

   _____

   _____

   2
   1
   0

7. Explain **in your own words** why the mother, in welcoming the aunt, spoke with just a little "tone" in her voice.

   _____

   _____

   2
   1
   0

8. (*a*) What impression of cousin Walter is given in Paragraph 12?

   _____

   2
   0

   (*b*) How does the writer prepare us for this image of Walter earlier in this section?

   _____

   _____

   2
   1
   0

Look at Paragraphs 16 to 18.

9. Explain **in your own words**:

   (*a*) in what **two** ways the father reacted to the guests;

   _____

   _____

   2
   1
   0

   (*b*) why in each case this was unusual.

   _____

   _____

   2
   1
   0

[Turn over

Official SQA Past Papers

10. **Quote** an expression which shows that the narrator tried to find out about his cousin in a secretive way.

_____

2
0

11. "He was odd-looking . . ."

Explain **in your own words** what the narrator seemed to think was the strangest thing about his cousin.

_____

_____

2
1
0

12. What does the last sentence of Paragraph 18 tell us about Walter's character?

_____

2
0

Look at Paragraphs 19 to 24.

13. **Using your own words**, explain why the narrator gave so many details about his aunt.

_____

_____

2
1
0

14. " 'Of course,' she repeated, just to herself, under her breath."

What does this suggest the mother thought of the aunt's tales of travel?

_____

2
0

Look at Paragraph 25.

15. **According to the narrator**, what were the **two** possible reasons for the relatives' visits? **Answer in your own words**.

(i) _____

_____

2
1
0

(ii) _____

_____

2
1
0

Look at Paragraphs 26 to 31.

16. "... how unalike they seemed!"

    Give details of **two** obvious contrasts between the aunt and the mother.

    (i) _____

    _____

    2
    0

    (ii) _____

    _____

    2
    0

17. What does the writer's use of the word "posturings" (Paragraph 27) tell you about the behaviour of the people in the room?

    _____

    _____

    2
    0

Think about the passage as a whole.

18. Why do you think the writer makes frequent use of brackets throughout the passage?

    _____

    _____

    2
    0

19. The narrator began to feel "like a stranger" in his own home. (Paragraph 31)

    By close reference to the text, show how his feelings towards his aunt changed.

    _____

    _____

    _____

    2
    1
    0

[END OF QUESTION PAPER]

[BLANK PAGE]

[BLANK PAGE]

[BLANK PAGE]

F G C

0860/107

SCOTTISH
CERTIFICATE OF
EDUCATION
1999

FRIDAY, 30 APRIL
9.15 AM – 10.30 AM

ENGLISH
STANDARD GRADE
Foundation, General
and Credit Levels
Writing

Read This First

1   Inside this booklet, there are photographs and words.
    Use them to help you when you are thinking about what to write.
    Look at all the material and think about all the possibilities.

2   There are 23 assignments altogether for you to choose from.

3   Decide which assignment you are going to attempt.
    Choose only **one** and write its number in the margin of your answer book.

4   Pay close attention to what you are asked to write.
    Plan what you are going to write.
    Read and check your work before you hand it in.
    Any changes to your work should be made clearly.

FIRST   **Look at the pictures opposite.**

NEXT   Think about growing up.

WHAT YOU HAVE TO WRITE

1. "A voyage of discovery" is another way of describing childhood.

   Write about your most important childhood discoveries.

   OR

2. **Write about** the ways your experience of growing up has influenced **your** views on bringing up children.

   OR

3. Pop stars are good rôle models for young people.

   Discuss this view.

   OR

4. Think about a time you were separated from a member of your family.

   Write about your thoughts and feelings when this happened.

[Turn over

FIRST   **Look at the picture opposite.**

NEXT   Think about appearances
               both usual and unusual.

| WHAT YOU HAVE TO WRITE |

---

5. "I can't because everyone will look at me."

   Write about a time when you had to overcome shyness.
   Concentrate on your **thoughts** and **feelings**.

   OR

6. Extreme fashion can cause conflict
   between young people and their parents,
   for example music, clothes and body image.

   Discuss.

   OR

7. "Individual but all the same."

   Write about how **you** cope with pressure from
   friends to go along with their ideas and
   interests.

   OR

8. "You're not going out like that!"

   Write a short story *or* **a personal account**
   or **a drama script** suggested by these words.

   OR

9. **Write a short story** with the title
   "Behind the Mask".

                                                    [Turn over

FIRST   **Look at the pictures opposite.**

NEXT   Think about gambling and its effects.

WHAT YOU HAVE TO WRITE

10. **Write an article** for a teenage magazine
    outlining the dangers gambling can have
    for young people.

    OR

11. **Write a short story** in which the central character
    gets involved in gambling to try to solve
    his or her problems.

    OR

12. "Spend, spend, spend."

    If **you** were to win a large sum of money
    how would you make use of it?

    OR

13. "A gamble that paid off?"

    Write about a time you took a chance . .

[Turn over

Page eight

FIRST   **Look at the picture opposite.**

NEXT   Think about people and challenges.

WHAT YOU HAVE TO WRITE

14. "Those who work in the emergency services should not have to risk their lives to rescue people who take part in dangerous activities."

   Discuss this point of view.

   OR

15. "A holiday with a difference."

   Write about an activity holiday you have taken part in.

   OR

16. **Write a short story** in which leadership plays an important part.

   OR

17. In search of . . .

   Write about what **you** are looking and hoping for from life.

[Turn over

FIRST   **Look at the pictures opposite.**

NEXT   Think about dance and entertainment.

WHAT YOU HAVE TO WRITE

---

18. A hobby? A competitive event?
     A form of keep fit? A good night out?
     An important part of your culture?

   Write about which **one** of these is true
   of dance for **you**.

   OR

19. Entertaining can be hard work.
     Have you ever taken part in a show or a musical
     as a performer, organiser or backstage worker?

   Write about your experience of **one** of these.

   OR

20. "Stage Fright"
     Using this as a title

   EITHER write a short story

   OR write about a personal experience.

   [Turn over for assignments 21 to 23 on *Page twelve*

There are no pictures for these assignments.

21. **Write about** the scene brought to mind by
     one of the following:

     ". . . fairer than the evening air,
     Clad in the beauty of a thousand stars"

     Christopher Marlowe

     OR

     "All bright and glittering in the smokeless air"

     William Wordsworth

     OR

     "Now fades the glimmering landscape on the sight,
     And all the air a solemn stillness holds"

     Thomas Gray

     OR

22. **Write a short story** with the title
     "The Broken Promise".

     OR

23. The only hope for our future
     lies in people caring more.

     Discuss.

[END OF QUESTION PAPER]

0860/407

NATIONAL
QUALIFICATIONS
2000

TUESDAY, 16 MAY
9.00 AM – 10.15 AM

ENGLISH
STANDARD GRADE
Foundation, General
and Credit Levels
Writing

Read This First

1   Inside this booklet, there are photographs and words.
    Use them to help you when you are thinking about what to write.
    Look at all the material and think about all the possibilities.

2   There are 18 assignments altogether for you to choose from.

3   Decide which assignment you are going to attempt.
    Choose only **one** and write its number in the margin of your answer book.

4   Pay close attention to what you are asked to write.
    Plan what you are going to write.
    Read and check your work before you hand it in.
    Any changes to your work should be made clearly.

SCOTTISH
QUALIFICATIONS
AUTHORITY

MCB 0860/407 6/68120

FIRST   **Look at the picture opposite.
               It shows the figure of Justice.**

NEXT   Think about crime and punishment.

WHAT YOU HAVE TO WRITE

---

1. "It wisnae me!"

   Write about a time when you were wrongly accused.

   Explain the circumstances and your thoughts and feelings.

   OR

2. "Let the punishment fit the crime."

   "It's time for a crack down."

   "Zero Tolerance."

   Should crime be tackled in a more forceful way?

   Discuss.

   OR

3. Choose **one** of the following titles and **write in any way** about:

   Crime Doesn't Pay   The Trial   The Verdict

[Turn over

FIRST   **Look at the picture opposite.**

NEXT   Think about people and animals.

WHAT YOU HAVE TO WRITE

---

4. **Describe** a person you know, who is interesting but different.

   OR

5. "It's not just a pet."

   Write about an animal which makes you feel this way.

   OR

6. "A nation of animal lovers."

   Are we? **Discuss**.

[Turn over

Agree

"Certainly, I would agree that . . ."

Against

"Not everyone however believes .

Persuasive

"Let's look at this together."

Argument

"The arguments really need to be fully explored."

Discuss

Balanced

"You've just got to look at both sides to be fair."

Oppose

"You may disagree but . . ."

Debate

"An explanation is really needed before it would be possible to decide."

For

"All the evidence suggests that . . ."

Question

"Is it possible to consider the point that . . .

FIRST   **Look at the page opposite.**
It gives a range of words connected with discussion.

NEXT   Think about topics on which people have strong opinions.

WHAT YOU HAVE TO WRITE

7. **Choose one** topic on which you hold strong views.

   Make clear your opinion on your chosen topic, taking some
   account of the views of others.

[Turn over

Page eight

FIRST   **Look at the pictures opposite.**
             They show how photographers from the media can
             intrude into the lives of other people.

NEXT   Think about how the camera can affect people's lives.

WHAT YOU HAVE TO WRITE

8. "From the man in the street to the rich and famous—hasn't
   everyone the right to a private life?"

   Discuss the effect of media "interest" on people's lives.

   OR

9. Choose **one** of the photographs opposite and
   write the story behind the picture.

   OR

10. Write about a photograph which has special
    memories for you.

                                                        [Turn over

FIRST   **Look at the picture opposite.**
               It shows both a telephone and computer hardware.

NEXT   Think about modern communication and technology.

WHAT YOU HAVE TO WRITE

    11. "Computers are fun."

        Write about your experience of using computers
        in your leisure time.

    OR

    12. Discuss one of these topics:

        Modem madness: the dangers of surfing the net.

    or

        The mobile phone: a blessing or a curse?

    OR

    13. Write a short story using **one** of the following titles:

        The Message   I've Got Your Number   The Hacker

[Turn over for assignments 14 to 18 on *Page twelve*

There are no pictures for these assignments.

14. Choose **one** of the following and **write in any way you wish**:

    "Things can only get better."

    D:Ream

    OR

    "Search for the hero inside yourself."

    M People

    OR

    "We are the generation that's got to be heard."

    Robbie Williams

    OR

15. "Preparation prevents poor performance."
    Everyone has to go through interviews.
    Explain clearly what you consider to be the important steps in preparation.

    OR

16. "Today's parents need to attend parenting classes
    in order to bring up their children properly."
    Do you agree? **Discuss**.

    OR

17. **Describe** the scene or person suggested to you by **one**
    of the following:
    " . . . The sun treads the path
    among cedars and enormous oaks."

    Gillian Clarke

    OR

    "she sat down
    at the scoured table
    in the swept kitchen
    beside the dresser with its cracked delft."

    Liz Lochhead

    OR

    "Pale rain over the dwindling harbour
    And over the sea wet church."

    Dylan Thomas

    OR

18. You have been asked to choose **five** items to put in a time capsule.
    Which five items would you choose and why?

[END OF QUESTION PAPER]

NATIONAL
QUALIFICATIONS
2001

MONDAY, 14 MAY
9.00 AM – 10.15 AM

ENGLISH
STANDARD GRADE
Foundation, General
and Credit Levels
Writing

Read This First

1   Inside this booklet, there are photographs and words.
    Use them to help you when you are thinking about what to write.
    Look at all the material and think about all the possibilities.

2   There are 23 assignments altogether for you to choose from.

3   Decide which assignment you are going to attempt.
    Choose only **one** and write its number in the margin of your answer book.

4   Pay close attention to what you are asked to write.
    Plan what you are going to write.
    Read and check your work before you hand it in.
    Any changes to your work should be made clearly.

SCOTTISH
QUALIFICATIONS
AUTHORITY

©

FIRST   **Look at the picture opposite.**
         It shows a grandmother reading a story to her grandson.

NEXT   Think about families and relationships.

WHAT YOU HAVE TO WRITE

1. **Write about** a person who has had the greatest influence on you and your life so far and explain why.

    OR

2. The older generation has nothing to teach the younger generation.
   Discuss.

    OR

3. Write about a single occasion when you had to make a choice between your family and your friends.

    OR

4. Write a **short story** using the title:
   Older and Wiser.

[Turn over

FIRST   **Look at the picture opposite.**
           It shows a group of people on a roller coaster.

NEXT   Think about excitement and entertainment.

WHAT YOU HAVE TO WRITE

5. **Write about** a time in your life when you were involved in something which made you feel **both excited** and **frightened** at the same time.

    OR

6. The experience of a lifetime.

    Write an article for a school magazine about an activity which was, for you, "the experience of a lifetime".

    OR

7. "Theme parks—value for money?"

    Do you agree? **Discuss.**

    OR

8. **Write a short story** using the title:
    Life is Full of Ups and Downs.

[Turn over

FIRST   **Look at the picture opposite.**

NEXT   Think about looking and seeing.

| WHAT YOU HAVE TO WRITE |

9. "No one knows the real me."

   Explain how you see yourself as opposed to how others may see you.

   OR

10. "You can be alone even in a crowd."

    Write about a time when you felt this way.

    OR

11. "CCTV—a good security device or a restriction of personal freedom?"

    What in your opinion are the benefits and drawbacks of closed circuit television? **Discuss.**

    OR

12. **Write in any way you wish** using the picture opposite as your inspiration.

                                                                    [Turn over

FIRST   **Look at the picture opposite.**
         It shows a couple beside an area blocked off by the police.

NEXT   Think about feelings to do with danger and safety.

WHAT YOU HAVE TO WRITE

13. **Write about** your thoughts and feelings at a time when you were
    reunited safely with someone special.

    OR

14. "Our towns and cities are no longer safe places to live and work."
    Discuss.

    OR

15. Write a **newspaper report** using the headline:
    STREET SEALED OFF!

    OR

16. **Write about an occasion** when the police were helpful
    to you or a member of your family.

                                                              [Turn over

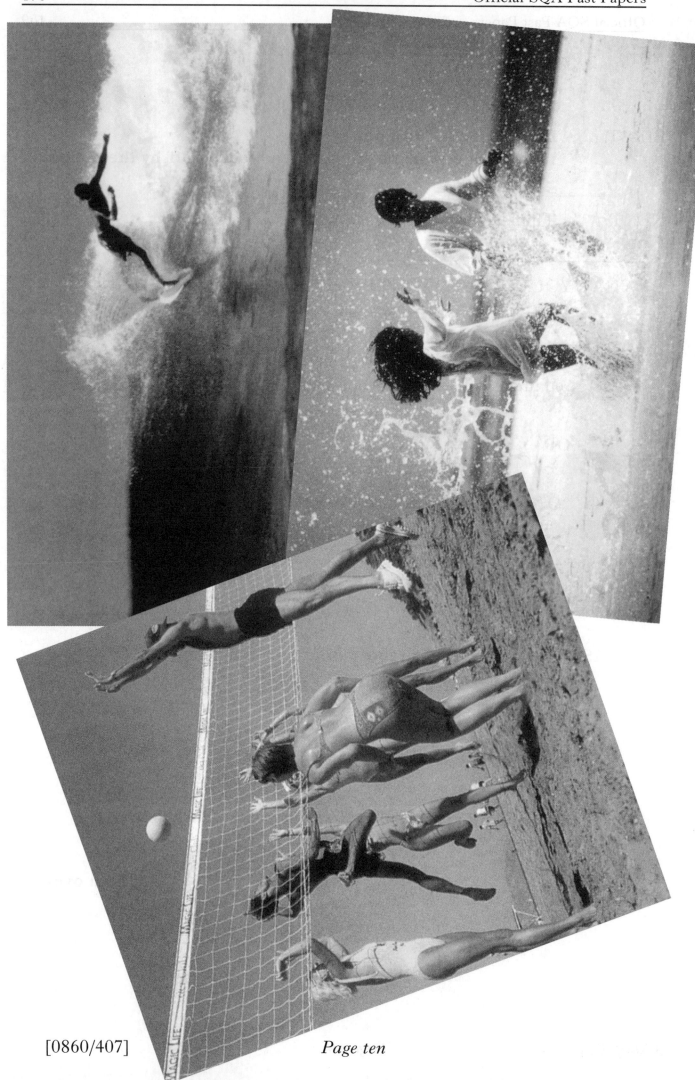

FIRST   **Look at the pictures opposite.**
         They show a variety of beach activities.

NEXT   Think about holidays.

> ## WHAT YOU HAVE TO WRITE

17. Write about a beach holiday which you **did or did not** enjoy and which holds vivid memories for you.

    OR

18. Some of our beaches and the sea are said to be no longer safe to use.

    Write a letter to a newspaper complaining about the state of a beach you have visited and making suggestions on how it can be improved.

    OR

19. Everyone seems to want to go abroad on holiday these days.

    Discuss the reasons why you think this is so.

    OR

20. **Write in any way you wish** using **one** of the following titles:

    The Wave   All at Sea   Undercurrents

    [Turn over for assignments 21 to 23 on *Page twelve*

There are no pictures for these assignments.

21. "Children aren't children for long these days. They are in too much of a hurry to grow up."

    Is this a fair statement? **Discuss**.

    OR

22. Choose **one** of the following and **describe the scene** it brings to mind:

    When men were all asleep the snow came flying,
    In large white flakes falling on the city brown,
    Stealthily and perpetually settling and loosely lying,
            Hushing the latest traffic of the drowsy town;

    Robert Bridges

    OR

    The trees are undressing, and fling in many places—
    On the grey road, the roof, the window-sill—
    Their radiant robes and ribbons and yellow laces;
    A leaf each second so is flung at will,
    Here, there another and another, is still and still.

    Thomas Hardy

    OR

    The sky is darkening like a stain;
    Something is going to fall like rain,
            And it won't be flowers

    W.H. Auden

    OR

23. **Write in any way you wish** using the title:
    The Outcast.

                    [*END OF QUESTION PAPER*]